W9-BRZ-700

THE ECONOMICS OF IRRIGATION

RELEASE

THE
ECONOMICS OF
IRRIGATION

BY

COLIN CLARK

*Director, University of Oxford Agricultural
Economics Research Institute*

96160

HD 1714
.C59

ST. JOSEPH'S UNIVERSITY · STX
HD1714.C59
The economics of irrigation.

3 9353 00167 5303

RELEASED

PERGAMON PRESS
OXFORD · LONDON · EDINBURGH · NEW YORK
TORONTO · SYDNEY · PARIS · BRAUNSCHWEIG

Pergamon Press Ltd., Headington Hill Hall, Oxford
4 & 5 Fitzroy Square, London W.1.
Pergamon Press (Scotland) Ltd., 2 & 3 Teviot Place, Edinburgh 1
Pergamon Press Inc., 44–01 21st Street, Long Island City, New York 11101
Pergamon of Canada, Ltd., 6 Adelaide Street East, Toronto, Ontario
Pergamon Press (Aust.) Pty. Ltd., 20–22 Margaret Street, Sydney, N.S.W.
Pergamon Press S.A.R.L., 24 rue des Écoles, Paris 5e
Vieweg & Sohn GmbH, Burgplatz 1, Braunschweig

Copyright © 1967
Pergamon Press Ltd.

First edition 1967

Library of Congress Catalog No. 67-15604

Printed in Great Britain by A. Wheaton & Co. Ltd., Exeter and London

(3172/67)

CONTENTS

v

PREFACE

THIS book is addressed to all those who may have any responsibility for spending money on irrigation, whether for small schemes or large, whether private or public, whether in arid or in humid climates, and whether their responsibility is direct, or the indirect responsibility which falls upon those who help to form political and business opinion.

It does not deal with the theory of water charges, or of the allocation of water to different uses, subjects on which there are many writings of great refinement—unfortunately, as often happens elsewhere, refinement and sterility seem to go together. It is intended as a piece of applied economics, collecting the critically important facts over as wide a range as the author has found possible. The standards of accuracy and comprehensiveness thus attained will, it is expected, soon be surpassed by other writers; but meanwhile it is hoped that it will be of some use.

Knowledge is pre-supposed of only the simplest principles of economics, of the distinction between money and real costs, of the distinction between marginal and average costs and products, and of the applicability of the principle of opportunity costs when comparing hydro-electric and thermal electrical generation in developing countries, as opposed to the questionable methods of costing per kilowatt hour generally used by electrical engineers.

Many unjustified claims have been and are being made for particular irrigation projects.

> Because water supply decisions are largely made in the political arena rather than in the market place, there is a great incentive for special-interest groups to obscure the real issues involved in government-subsidized water projects and to exploit public romanticism for 'making the desert bloom even as the rose', thus obtaining public support for their own financial gain.[1]

Some advocates of irrigation not only fail to understand

economics, but the simplest principles of accounting as well, and are unable even to distinguish gross from net returns.

Little attention need now be paid to the supposed beneficial secondary economic effects of large irrigation schemes. There was some justification for making such a case in the 1930s, when a great deal of labour and other productive resources were unemployed, and might have been capable of being put to work through the indirect effects of a large irrigation scheme. Even in times or places of widespread unemployment, however, it is necessary to consider the relative merits of irrigation, and of alternative projects for spending the same amount of capital, which would also give much the same beneficial secondary effects. In much of the world as it is now, when most productive resources which are employable are already fully employed, or over-employed, the secondary economic effects of large capital expenditures may even be harmful. Irrigation schemes must now be judged, therefore, on their direct economic costs and returns.

Not all irrigation is uneconomic. Irrigation from wells has proved economic for a number of crops, so long as the well is not too deep, and so long as power pumping is possible—the lifting of water by man or bullock labour is uneconomic even under Indian conditions, except from very shallow wells. Small dams, if carefully designed, usually prove economic, but the economic results from large dams, which can supply water and generate power (and also generate extreme political emotion) are extremely variable. Some are abundantly justifiable economically, others equally clearly not.

On the water requirements of plants, we are bound to take account of some important conclusions reached by Dr. Penman, F.R.S., who has shown that under given climatic conditions the daily water requirements of all crops will be much the same. This runs counter to many of the previous ideas of irrigation administrators, and of course immediately leads the economist to the conclusion that, daily requirements of all crops being much the same, and water usually being the scarce factor, irrigation land should be used for those crops which give the highest economic value per day of growing season. This principle is found to be borne out when we examine the available information on net financial returns to irrigation, which are most satisfactory in the case of high value crops grown in economically advanced countries. For India, and countries in a similar position, the information is not adequate, but what we have shows rather discouraging results. In the use of irrigation, it appears, "unto everyone that hath shall be given".

Hopes are now being expressed of widespread use of irrigation water obtained by desalination of the sea. Even with the most modern equipment now in prospect, the costs of such water will be far above those which any irrigation farmer is willing to pay, though they will be within reach of that which municipal authorities in dry areas are willing to pay for household water supplies.

CHAPTER 1

DEFINITIONS

IRRIGATION is defined as the application of water, by human agency, to assist the growth of crops and grass. In general, the word does not cover the other objects for which man stores and controls the flow of water, that is to say, for household and industrial water supplies, for hydro-electric power, for the provision of navigable channels, and also the getting rid of unwanted water, in flood measures, and in the draining of swamps and waterlogged land. These other objects, however, may sometimes share with irrigation the use of works, equipment, waterflows and administrative organisation; and they therefore have an indirect effect upon the economics of irrigation. Irrigation water may be (1) pumped from underground sources by means of wells, (2) drawn from the natural flow of streams, (3) obtained by damming or otherwise regulating the flow of streams. It may be applied to the crop by flooding, by channels, or by spray.

Professional irrigation engineers, in English-speaking countries, are accustomed to thinking in terms of acres, acre-feet and cusecs, and may be inconvenienced by having to translate these units into 0·405 hectares, 1234 cubic metres, or 895,000 cubic metres per year, respectively. But this inconvenience will be outweighed by the far greater ease, for all those who are not professional irrigation engineers, with which problems can be grasped when stated in metric units. A million cubic metres of irrigation water, when applied to a depth of one metre (quite a usual depth), will irrigate exactly one square kilometre, or a metre of rainfall on the same area will represent another million cubic metres. British units are not so conveniently inter-related. The unit in which all quantities of water will be expressed is the cubic metre (for which m³ is the customary abbreviation).

The following conversion factors may be useful:

1 cent/cubic metre	=	$12·34/acre-foot
1 cusec/square mile/year	=	34·5 centimetres depth/year
1 kilogram/hectare	=	0·89 lb/acre

Economic values also are originally expressed in pounds and rupees and dollars, and each currency has had very different purchasing powers at different dates. We need a single unit in terms of which they can all be expressed. For construction costs, and all other goods and services except agricultural products, the most convenient unit for international comparisons is that which has been used by the O.E.C.D. for their comparisons of national products in Europe, namely the quantity of goods and services exchangeable for $1 in U.S.A. in 1950. It is brought up to date, by a factor of 1·342, to the current (beginning of 1964) purchasing power of the dollar. All economic values henceforward are given in dollars and cents,* on the understanding that money values from other countries (and from U.S.A. at past dates) have been converted to current dollars in accordance with the *purchasing power* of the money (which is not always the same as its exchange rate). It may be repeated that this is a unit of volume of actual goods and services used, produced or exchanged, and NOT a unit of money.

The following table gives, for early 1964, the purchasing power, in current dollar units, of the currencies of some leading countries using irrigation.

Peso Mexico	£ U.K.	£ Australian	New franc France	000 lire Italy	Rupee India, Pakistan	Escudo[a] Portugal	£ Egyptian
0·28	3·29	2·36	0·25	1·88	0·25	0·061	4·40

[a] Of 1955 purchasing power.

For agricultural products, on the other hand, United States prices are often well out of line with those prevailing elsewhere.

* Abbreviated as $ (dollar) and c (cent).

The natural unit in this case is the kilogram of wheat, all other agricultural products being expressed as wheat in terms of the relative prices prevailing in the local markets. We use this economic conversion factor, not the relative calorific value, which would unduly depreciate some high-protein and other agricultural products.

CHAPTER 2

WATER REQUIREMENTS OF PLANTS

QUITE recently, much to the surprise of irrigation engineers and farmers accustomed to thinking in terms of each crop having its own "water requirement", Penman (of the Rothamsted Laboratory of Soil Physics) has established the theorem, based on the simple laws of physics, that water requirements for all crops must be about the same, if they are grown on the same soil and for the same growing season. The physics of the matter are quite clear. Inside the plant, the functions performed by water are innumerable. But the quantity of water directly required for these purposes is limited; virtually the whole of the plant's marginal requirements for water are to transpire in order to keep its temperature down within its limit of toleration.

The old idea that each plant had a "transpiration ratio", or given amount of dry matter which must be grown per unit of water transpired, has been abandoned by botanists; it is now recognised that, for a given growth of dry matter, the amount of water transpired may vary greatly according to climate and circumstances. If the maximum temperature is not to be exceeded—that is to say, if the plants are to live—the cultivation must have a "thermal balance", with the heat inflow from solar radiation, a small amount conducted upwards from the earth, and sometimes from hot winds, balanced by the heat outflow through radiation and convection, the effect of cooling winds, and heat stored in the soil to be disposed of at night. The balance of heat must, inescapably, be disposed of in the form of evaporation from the soil and transpiration from the plants.

The factors in this thermal balance, it is clear, are very

complex. Thornwaite[2]* has devised a system of predicting evaporation approximately from available climatic statistics, which has been checked satisfactorily against the known volume of evaporation of water from certain American irrigation areas, but which may not be of universal applicability. Twelve valleys in the United States were studied with the figure for theoretical evaporation (averaged over the year) ranging from 1·2 to 3·2 mm/day. Actual figures were found to be within 4% of theoretical in all cases except West Tule Lake in California (actual figure 15% in excess of theoretical). The Barahona Valley in the Dominican Republic, in a much hotter climate, showed a theoretical annual average of 4 mm/day, which was precisely confirmed in fact.

What is, however, clear is that nearly all these factors determining evaporation are independent, or virtually independent, of the nature of the crop being grown.† The climatic factors— solar radiation, wind movements, etc.—are entirely independent. The temperature limits which have to be observed do not vary greatly between plants—some naturally occurring desert plants have a higher temperature limit, but they are not of agricultural importance. There is a significant but minor factor in that some plants (e.g. sugar cane) have glossier leaves than others, and are therefore able to reflect back a little more of the sun's radiation, thus slightly reducing their water requirements. Tree crops, and a few others in their earlier stages of growth, may leave a proportion of the land uncovered by vegetation, and this again may effect some reduction in water requirements, as the bare soil can be allowed to rise to a higher temperature than the growing plant. (Even this advantage, however, is not quite what it seems; a plant surrounded by bare ground may thereby transpire more because of advection of warm air from adjacent areas.)

---

* See also the "Blaney–Criddle System", devised in California for predicting water requirements. Also an interesting formula suggested by Quesnel (*Comptes Rendues de l'Academie d'Agriculture de France*, 6 June 1962) to the effect that with solar radiation at the rate of R calories/cm² horizontal surface/day and average monthly temperature $T°$ Centigrade then potential evapotranspiration in mm/month will be $0·4(R + 50)T/(T + 15)$.

† This refers, of course, to water loss per day—crops with a longer growing season naturally require more water in total.

To state the matter more fully, direct transfer of heat between the soil and the atmosphere is controlled by the difference of their temperatures, the wind speed, and the roughness of the soil. Evaporation also depends upon wind speed and the roughness of the crop, its average height above the ground, saturation vapour pressure at current temperature, and difference of vapour pressure between crop and atmosphere. Reflection coefficients are now estimated to be as high as $0 \cdot 25$ for most crops, and probably for trees too, as against $0 \cdot 05$ for an open water surface.[3] Evaporation from the Nile swamps, whose surface presumably does not reach the high summer temperatures of the land in Sudan, is estimated at $6 \cdot 1$ mm/day (annual average) whether from papyrus-covered or open water surface (the roughness of the papyrus about offsets its reflection coefficient).

The point is illustrated by observations[4] in a rice field in the Sudan.

TABLE 1

Evaporation or Evapo-transpiration in Sudan (mm/day)

	June	July	August	September	October
Evaporation from open ground	14	14	13	10	6
Evapo-transpiration from rice field			14–15	10	7·5
Evaporation from bare earth surrounded by rice			11	7	4

The summer temperatures and evaporation must be about the highest in the world. Subject to this consideration, the bare soil, it is seen, can be allowed to rise to a higher temperature than the planted. The lower figures in the last line show that the rice plants nearby keep the soil cooler than a plain open field. This is the reason why experiments conducted with single pot plants, with open space around them, do not reproduce the thermal conditions of the field, and *overstate* the plant's water requirements.

The complete unreliability of pot experiments, which fail to reproduce the thermal conditions of the open field, is illustrated by Bernard's experiments on growing Bahia grass in Belgian Congo,[5] which when grown in pots showed evaporation ranging from 3 to 9 mm/day, closely proportioned to leaf area; but a year's lysimeter tests in the field showed a uniform evaporation of approximately 1·1 m (3 mm/day), whether growing naturally, watered, or watered and fertilised. In the two latter experiments the yields were raised to 44 and 63 tons dry matter/hectare/year respectively, without altering the water requirement significantly.

Penman's researches—or, if we like to put it that way, his pointing out of an obvious fact of physics, which we should have recognised earlier—must necessarily lead to the drastic revision of all previous ideas about the economics of irrigation. Irrigating a given area, at a given time of the year, will use up the same amount of water almost irrespective of the crop which is being grown; irrigators therefore should always be growing the crop which, at that time of the year, and at the prices then prevailing, yields the highest economic return per unit of area and per unit of time. In general, this does not appear to have been the policy in the past. Charges for a given amount of water have often been differentiated in such a way as to encourage the growing of the less economic crops.

This matter was keenly debated, for instance, in the Murrumbidgee area in Australia, where at one time rice took two-thirds of the entire water supply available for the whole area, but yielded a comparatively low return for each unit of water used. Extravagant use of water on rice was encouraged by the price charged, namely 0·2 c/m³* as against 0·4 for other growers on water whose cost (including maintenance and interest, but no redemption of capital) was 0·8. Often in Australia users of water are charged maintenance costs only (if even that), all interest and capital charges falling on the state treasuries.

During recent years in the Murrumbidgee irrigation area the proportion of the total water supply devoted to rice has been reduced to approximately one-half. However, the amount of irrigation water received by the rice is still excessive.

* Cents per cubic metre.

B

TABLE 2

Plants' Supposed Water Requirements

Crop	Country	Months' growing season	Supposed water requirements cm/month	Do. net (from lysimeter tests)
Bananas	Israel	12	17	
Orchards	Iraq	12	14	
	Israel	12	11	
	Italy	12	7	
	Pakistan N.W. Frontier	12	7½	
Lucerne and pasture	Israel	12	14	
	Australia	12	13	
	Italy (lucerne)	9	12	
	Italy (grass)	9	10	
Forest	Pakistan Punjab	12	9	
Sugar cane	Pakistan	11	12	
	Pakistan N.W. Frontier	11	14	
	Pakistan Punjab	11	13	12
	Pakistan Punjab	11	12	10½
Cotton	Pakistan	7	14	
	Israel	8	16	
	Iraq	7	20	
	Pakistan Punjab	7	12½	14
	Pakistan Punjab	7	14	12
Rice	General (see above)	7	21½	
	Pakistan	7	15	
	Pakistan Punjab	7	27	19
	Pakistan Punjab	7	27	14
	Pakistan Punjab	7	21	16
Wheat	Pakistan	6	6	
	Pakistan N.W. Frontier	8	8	
	Iraq (including barley)	6	11	
	Pakistan Punjab	6	4	5
	Pakistan Punjab	6	7	7
	Pakistan Punjab	6	3½	4
Sugar-beet	Israel	6½	15	
	Italy	6½	15	
Fodder crops	Iraq (winter berseem)	6	14	
	Iraq (summer)	5	25	

TABLE 2 *(cont.)*

Crop	Country	Months' growing season	Supposed water requirements cm/month	Do. net (from lysimeter tests)
Fodder crops *(cont.)*	Pakistan N.W. Frontier (summer)	4	16	
	Israel (winter, berseem)	3½	25	
	Pakistan Punjab (winter berseem)	3	16	12
	Pakistan Punjab (winter, pigeon pea)	3	9	9
	Pakistan (pigeon pea)	3	18	
Maize	Israel	6	14	
	Italy	6	15	
	Pakistan	6	10	
	Pakistan N.W. Frontier	6	11	
	Pakistan Punjab	6	8	8
	Pakistan Punjab	6	9	6
Tobacco	Israel	5	19	
	Australia	4	27	
Tomatoes	Israel	5	36	
Groundnuts	Israel	4½	25	
Millet	Iraq	3	19	
	Pakistan	3	18	
Melons	Israel	3½	27	
Vegetables	Israel	3	33	
Potatoes	Israel	3	17	
	Italy	3	30	
Early potatoes	Israel	2	15	
Barley	Pakistan	6	6	
Sorghum	Pakistan	6	10	
Oilseed	Pakistan	6	6	

Sources:

Australia	See reference (6)
Iraq	See references (7) and (8)
Israel	See references (9) and (10)
Italy	See reference (11)
Pakistan	See reference (12)
Punjab	See reference (13)
N.W. Frontier Province	See references (7) and (14)

In Table 2 the length of growing season (known or estimated) is compared with statements of supposed water requirements by a number of authorities (these latter sometimes omit the natural rainfall, which has then had to be estimated).

Some interesting lysimeter experiments in the Punjab in 1946–7 and 1947–8 measured the addition of water to the sub-soil (recoverable by pumping), or loss of water from the subsoil, as the case might be, with varying water supplies; the water requirements so calculated are shown in the table, where appropriate.

We see a number of cases of serious over-watering, and perhaps a tendency to under-water maize and wheat. Otherwise, the monthly figures (adjusted in some cases after lysimeter tests) appear on the average to be more or less what was to have been expected, in view of varying temperatures. A serious case[15] of over-watering is reported from the Indian State of Maharashtra, where sugar-cane (crop cycle 18 months) receives an average of 32 cm/month (including 4–5 in. rainfall). The Sena Sugar Estates in Mozambique[16] which have to provide for a dry season, installed sprays with a maximum capacity of 8 m/day, or 24 cm/month.

In specifying soil water requirements for plant growth, it does not serve much purpose to state only the proportion by volume of water in the soil (or, what comes to the same thing, the number of millimetres water per centimetre depth of soil, or inches water per foot depth). In any case, maximum water-holding capacity varies very greatly with types of soils, being at its lowest with coarse sands and at its highest with clay loams; and, moreover, plants usually do not need soil water content to be anywhere near capacity. The important coefficient is the amount of energy which the plant's roots have to exert in order to extract water from the soil; Schofield measured this by the logarithm of the height in centimetres of the imputed capillary column required to effect this extraction. This coefficient pF stands at 7 when the soil is oven-dry; under normal conditions may be about 2; a value of 4 indicates the "wilting-point" of plants (with a few exceptions such as cacti). It appears that this is the maximum energy which the plant can summon up for the purpose of extracting water from the soil. What is important is the amount of water held at tension less than 4 on Schofield's scale.

Some soil scientists, however, hold that the wilting-point occurs not through lack of energy on the part of the plant, but because water cannot travel rapidly enough through the zone adjacent to the roots. The first wilting-point, i.e. the pF at which crops wilt during the hottest part of the day, but recover at night, is perhaps that at which water movement through the soil is too slow to meet demands for transpiration. Ultimate wilting-point is usually measured at the point where the plant has become wholly and finally incapable of transpiration, even in a saturated atmosphere. The theory of the inability of water to travel fast enough through the soil may be criticised in the light of the consideration that pressure differences within the soil are small in comparison with the diffusion pressure between leaf and atmosphere.[17, 18]

Much further research is needed before we can measure the effect upon plant growth of a partial deficiency of water. Reutlinger and Seagraves,[19] in a pioneering study on sandy soils in North Carolina, showed that yields of tobacco (a shallow-rooting crop) fell more or less linearly from 2300 to 1500 kg/hectare in response to changes in the average over the whole growing season of a "soil moisture deficiency index". This index, which was elaborately constructed, depended on the choice, out of some twenty (!) alternative methods of measuring soil water deficiency, of Wiser's method,[20] which assumes, in effect, that water does not redistribute itself between soil layers when the water content of the soil is below capacity.

The operation of irrigation, and the planning of the amount and frequency of application of water, depends[21] on the effective depth of the soil (amount within range of the plants' roots), its holding capacity, and the rate at which it can absorb water without its running off, as well as the daily rate of evapotranspiration, which may be as low as $2\frac{1}{2}$ mm/day in cool humid climates, up to the high tropical figures quoted above.

The "effective depths" at which plant roots can extract moisture from the soil and other relevant data were stated by Molenaar* (for deep well-drained soils) and are shown in Table 3.

* Nye (Department of Soil Science, University of Oxford, private communication) also gives 60 cm for groundnuts, and 240 cm for lucerne (alfalfa). However, the plant obtains decreasing proportions of its water requirements from these deeper roots.

TABLE 3

Effective Depths for Plant Roots (cm)

Onion, lettuce	30
Pasture, potato, bean, cabbage, spinach, strawberry	60
Sweet corn, table beet, peas, squash, carrot, eggplant, peppers	90
Sugar-beet, sweet potato, cotton, citrus, lima bean, artichoke	120
Melon, flax, maize, small grains	150
Alfalfa, asparagus, non-citrus orchard, grapes, hops, grains other than maize, sudan grass, sorghum, tomato	180

	Water holding capacity (mm/cm depth of soil)	Maximum rate of water intake (mm/hr)
Very coarse sands	0·4	19 —25½
Sands	0·7	12½—19
Sandy loams	1·05	12½
Medium loams	1·6	10
Clay loams	1·75	7½
Clays	1·70	—

The effective storage capacity of a soil therefore, instead of being a uniform 10 cm, as Thornthwaite originally proposed, would appear from the above figures to vary from 1·2 cm for lettuces grown in sandy soil to 315 cm for sorghum or tomatoes grown in a clay loam.

This idea, however, would be strongly controverted by Penman, who believes that each plant does not have a fixed rooting depth, but tends to adapt it in inverse proportion to the water-holding capacity of the soil, so that the *effective* storage capacity of *all* types of soils tends to be nearly uniform for a *given* crop (though no doubt he would except a few crops such as onion and potato, which seem to be always shallow-rooted).

E. W. Russell,[22] on the whole, thinks the same. "Frequent light irrigations encourage shallow rooting, and infrequent heavy, deep rooting . . . because the roots can find all the water they need in the superficial layers of the soil . . . plants are usually deeper-rooted in light sandy than in clay or loam soils"; though he does also mention the possibility that roots may be repelled by the higher CO_2 concentration at the deeper levels in clay or loam soils.

In making the choice between frequent and infrequent irrigation, it should be borne in mind that it is probable (though there is not universal agreement on this point) that the rate of photosynthesis per unit of leaf area remains unaffected by temporary deficiencies; but frequent irrigation should give a larger leaf area. However, the capacity of leaves for photosynthesis is impaired by wilting—leaves sometimes do not regain photosynthetic capacity even after the wilting has been cured and the leaf has again become "turgid". This has been found to be the case with maize but not with sorghum. This difference appears to be the cause of the observed greater apparent drought resistance of the latter. The effect of inadequacy of water can be mitigated by the application of chemical fertilisers (the widely held view that the effects of drought are accentuated by such addition is the opposite of the truth).

That fertiliser, so far from increasing the plant's demand for water, can, in effect, serve as a "substitute" for water was brought out by an important study[23] on fertilised grass (Table 4). In this case, in view of the variability of the rainfall (the work was done in 1953, a fairly normal season with 338 mm rain from April to September) no predetermined amounts of water were used, but in the various experiments the rule was made to begin watering when the water deficit in the soil had reached 17, 34 and 51 mm respectively. In the best fertilised plots the grass did not seem to be much affected if watering was delayed till the 51 mm deficit, and the gain over the unirrigated land was much *less* than with the unfertilised or less fertilised grass.

TABLE 4

Combined Response to Fertilisers and Irrigation (grass dry weight tons/hectare/year)

	Unfertilised	Fertilised with 314 kg/hectare nitro chalk	Fertilised with 628 kg/hectare nitro-chalk
Unirrigated	8·5	11·2	14·0
Irrigated at			
51 mm deficit	9·7	12·2	15·2
34 mm deficit	10·3	13·1	15·3
17 mm deficit	10·8	13·2	15·6

In England we have six years' results[24] on barley (Table 5).

TABLE 5

Fertilised and Irrigated Barley

	Fertilised with 25 kg/hectare nitrogen (element)	Do. 50 kg/hectare
Tons/hectare yield		
Unirrigated	3·46	3·95
Irrigated	3·83	4·08

The more heavily fertilised crops again show less response to additional water. There is also general agreement that phosphatic fertilisers increase the crops' drought resistance, probably by accelerating their maturity. Nitrogenous fertilisers may be dangerous in some climates if they delay the plant's maturity beyond its normal growing season into a dry season—this may be the origin of the fear that they lead to a general increase in water needs.

Nix also holds, as do a number of soil scientists, that it is unwise to allow the reserve of water in the soil to fall below the point half-way between "maximum storage capacity" and "permanent wilting point", where the plant can extract no moisture at all from the soil—below this mid point plant growth is hindered, indeed impairment of growth is apparent at values of pF below that which an actual reduction of transpiration is observed.

Many irrigation engineers and administrators will still stoutly assert that the water requirements for a given area (or "duty", as it is sometimes called in India) vary greatly according to the nature of the crop.* But more careful examination shows—as indeed it must—that these differences arise

* Thus, for example, the Indian Ministry of Agriculture (*Studies in the Economy of Farm Management*, Madras 1954–5) definitely state the water requirements of rice at 1·31 m, of cotton at 0·38, of coarse grains (ragi, cholam and cumbu) at 0·36, 0·22 and 0·17 respectively. Ghulam Mohamed (*Pakistan Development Review*, Winter 1963, p. 513) states requirements at 0·7–0·8 m for rice, 0·35–0·45 for cotton. Sir M. MacDonald and Partners, in their Report No. 2 (1958) to the Government of Iraq on the Diyala and Middle Tigris Projects first estimate water requirements for the

from one of the following causes: (1) Some crops have a longer growing period; (2) some crops are grown at seasons of the year when solar radiation is greater; (3) the extent of the minor factors (leaf reflection and bare soil) mentioned above; (4) the fact that, even when all the other factors are the same, some crops are usually grown on lighter soils, where therefore there may be a much greater loss of water by seepage, than others.

Of all crops, rice is the most dependent upon irrigation, because the biology of the rice plant requires that the whole field should be actually under water during the planting season. Only under very rare circumstances can this result be brought about by natural rainfall, and in almost every case irrigation from streams or wells is necessary. Because they are high, and because of the great importance of the crop, the water requirements of rice have received more study[25] than those of most irrigation crops; in general, as will be seen below, our information about water consumption is still gravely inadequate. Average water requirements for rice in tropical climates have been estimated by the International Rice Commission at Bangkok[26] at 1·5 m in all. These are the combined requirements for flooding the field at planting and for growing the crop, and are met by the rainfall during the growing season, a small amount (probably 0·2 m maximum under the most favourable circumstances and with the most retentive soils) receivable from water previously stored in the soil, with the balance having to be met by irrigation. It may be added that the economic disadvantage of rice's high water requirements is in part offset by the fact that by using ponded water (derived from ground water if supplementation of rainfall is necessary) rice makes use of nutrients which have already been leached out of other soils and would have otherwise have been lost altogether to the basin. Also the waterlogging makes available

---

different seasons of the year on the Blaney–Criddle system, but then apply "crop factors" ranging from 0·6 for orchards and vegetables to 1·1 for rice. However, the effects of this differentiation are in the end cancelled out; total evaporation requirements (on the arable land, constituting some 85% of the settled area) are estimated at a fairly steady rate ranging between 1·1 and 1·4 m (annual rate), except for the November–February period, during which the rate ranges between 0·8 and 0·95.

phosphates which would not have been available to dry land crops. The seepage from the flooded rice fields moreover performs the valuable function of removing accumulated salts in basin-irrigation schemes (as in Egypt) on heavy clay. To achieve this object, ponding of water would be necessary in any case.

Needs may be much higher in clear dry climates where the day temperatures may be exceptional, and where there may be drying winds. Water requirements for rice have been estimated at 2·5 m in Central Asia and 1·8 m in the Murrumbidgee irrigation area in Australia (where excessive use was encouraged by an exceptionally favourable price). Water requirements in the dry clear summers of Spain and Italy also seem to be higher than in the humid cloudy tropics. (We must also take account of the possibility, however, that the soils in question in Central Asia and Australia are more porous than those usually used for rice growing.)

A figure of 1·9 was also estimated for Iraq, but the general estimate of about 1·5 was confirmed in two provinces of Pakistan. The experiment in India (quoted below) showed that *ad lib.* watering of rice, with total supplies up to 3½–4 m, did not increase yields in comparison with control plots with a supply of 1·6 m (in 5-day waterings).

The Californian Department of Public Works[27] conducted a series of lysimeter tests showing that evapotranspiration could range from 0·31 m/year on bare earth to 0·66 for natural vegetation and 0·88 for willow plantations, to 1·50 for an open water surface (Table 6). The figures for other crops show considerable variations, which nevertheless may be capable of explanation in terms of lengths of growing season and of the proportions of the ground left bare.

Grüner[28] considered that in Sicily, with a rainfall of about 0·7 m, orchards needed 0·2 m of irrigation, fodder crops 0·7—0·8. Ionides[29] estimated rates for Jordan (Table 7).

The effects of persistent watering to excess can be very serious indeed. Naylor made an important study[30] of the Khaipur area in West Pakistan. In the old days of irrigation from summer floods only, the fields received an average of 25 cm/year. With perennial irrigation, the water supply rose to 41 cm in summer and 28 cm in winter; now it is 46 cm and 41 cm respectively, or

TABLE 6

California, Evaporation (in metres)

	Growing season	Whole year
Celery	0·36	0·46
Haricot beans	0·41	0·65
Potato	0·46	0·64
Onion	0·49	0·65
Grass pasture	0·66	0·66
Fruit	0·69	0·76
Sugarbeet	0·70	0·86
Market gardens	0·73	0·80
Wheat	0·74	0·88
Asparagus	0·82	0·82
Lucerne	0·97	1·07

TABLE 7

Jordan, Evaporation (mm/day)

	7 warmer months	5 cooler months
Winter cereals	–	4
Vegetables	6	4
Citrus	3	2
Bananas	9	6

87 cm in all. This is more than can safely be put *regularly* on any soil without drainage. The soil is becoming waterlogged, i.e. the water table rises near enough to the surface to drown the plant roots, thus making the soil useless. It is estimated that only 2% of the gross water supply is added to the subsoil each year (40% used by crops, the rest evaporated from uncultivated ground); but this 2 cm/year of water is enough to saturate 9 cm of soil; and this is the rate at which the water table is rising. Spreading water over a wide area (which is often done for political reasons) leads to a further evil: "it speeds up the rate of soil salinisation, without eliminating the rising water table".

To obviate both waterlogging and salination* Naylor recommends concentrated watering at the rate of 1·2 m/year with adequate drainage either by power-operated tube wells capable of removing† 31 cm/year; or in some cases open drains, which can remove 21 cm/year.

Common sense tells us that there must be limits beyond which further water cannot usefully be added. It is useful, however, to have the results (Table 8) of two experiments in deliberate overwatering, on rice in India and lucerne in the United States.

TABLE 8

Experiments in Overwatering

	Total water input (metres)	Marginal return (kg milled rice or dried lucerne/m³) ‡
Rice		
Dry season: watering 5-daily	1·65 ⎫	
Watering continuously	4·02 ⎭	0·011
Wet season: watering 5-daily	1·58 ⎫	
Watering continuously	3·43 ⎭	0·024
Lucerne (Alfalfa)	0·62	
		1·94
	1·00	
		1·57
	1·25	
		negative
	Above 1·25	

Sources:

India   See reference (31).
U.S.A.   See reference (32).

* In non-saline areas water table should be 1 m plus rooting depth from the surface if capillary rise is to make no contribution to water supply of crops. In saline areas capillary tension plus osmotic tension due to surface salts both operate to bring water from water table to surface—drainage depth will have to be 1½ m or more, i.e. salination not only leads to salt accumulation but once it has occurred drainage depth has to be nearly doubled if trouble is not to get worse!

† At ordinary rates of diffusion in the soil, a single well of 2·7 million cm/year (or 3 cusecs) capacity, working 70% of the time, should suffice to drain 360 hectares.

‡ Physical quantity of additional crop obtained from further watering divided by the number of cubic metres of additional water used. 3-day watering of rice was also tried, but gave results similar to 5-day watering.

CHAPTER 3

ECONOMIC RETURNS TO IRRIGATION

WHAT is irrigation water worth to a farmer? It would be simple-minded to expect a single answer. We may expect widely different answers according to climates and according to crops grown. But we have not yet reached the end of the question. Even when we are dealing with a single climate, and a single pattern of farming, the principles of economic analysis still tell us that we must look for a demand curve, and price elasticities of demand (defined, where q is the quantity demanded and p is the price, as $\dfrac{dq/q}{dp/p}$, or the proportionate effect on demand of a change in price). The amount of water for which a farmer (we assume that he is intelligent and well-informed) can find remunerative use depends on the prices of his products, and of other inputs, and on the price at which water is offered to him. To take extreme cases, there must be some price so high as to compel him to do without water altogether; and if it comes gratis he will probably waste it. Within this range, the farmer has considerable freedom of choice as to the quantity of the more water-demanding crops he will cultivate; and also, for a given crop, the amount of water which it shall receive.

In the simpler stages of economic analysis, economists have tended to assume unchanging price elasticities of demand for any one commodity. It is now clear that this is not generally the case, and that price elasticities themselves may change considerably.

The demand curve for water may be measured in the first place empirically, by observation of the amounts demanded by farmers under varying circumstances; but also in a more sophisticated manner by linear programming. In this case, the agricultural economist, armed with all the information about

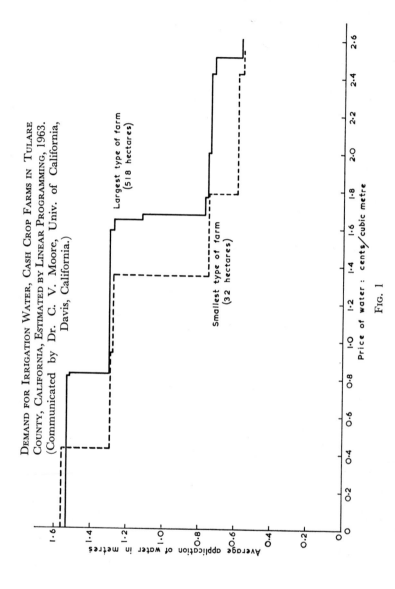

DEMAND FOR IRRIGATION WATER, CASH CROP FARMS IN TULARE COUNTY, CALIFORNIA, ESTIMATED BY LINEAR PROGRAMMING, 1963. (Communicated by Dr. C. V. Moore, Univ. of California, Davis, California.)

Largest type of farm (518 hectares)

Smallest type of farm (32 hectares)

Average application of water in metres

Price of water : cents/cubic metre

FIG. 1

costs of labour, fertilisers, etc., for each unit of crop production, each crop's responses to water, and the expected returns from it, sets out to tell the farmer precisely how much of each crop it is worth while for him to grow, with varying water prices.

The most direct measure of the economic value of irrigation water is found under those (very rare) circumstances when farmers are able and willing to exchange it among themselves. Such a situation arose[33] in North Colorado (a dry but fairly cool area) in 1959, and it was found that the prices ranged from $0 \cdot 2$ to $0 \cdot 4$ c/m³* early in the season, $0 \cdot 34$ to $0 \cdot 65$ late in the season. Anderson attempted to make an independent estimate of the value of water by linear programming. His lowest figure was $0 \cdot 73$ c/m³ for low value crops grown on poor soil, rising to $2 \cdot 6$ c/m³ for high value crops on good soil. There seems to have been some "buyer's rent" in the Colorado prices, i.e. water coming onto the market in times of unusual abundance, and purchased by buyers who would in fact have been willing to pay a much higher price for at any rate a substantial part of their supply.

Valuing the rupee at $0 \cdot 25$, water pumped from tube wells in West Pakistan is sold at 1 c/m³, the price falling to $0 \cdot 65$ as more wells are sunk and competition increases.[34]

A much more ambitious application[35] of linear programming to this problem was made in Tulare County, California, where cotton, beans and sugar-beet are the principal irrigated crops (Fig. 1). For supposed farms of various sizes (and for the whole county by combining these estimates) programmes were worked out on the assumption of varying water prices, showing the precise points at which the use of increased quantities of water became worth while. No great differences were found between the largest and smallest farms. For the county as a whole, a price elasticity of $0 \cdot 19$ was found at prices up to $1 \cdot 2$ c/m³, and of $0 \cdot 70$ at higher prices. (The figures include all water other than rainfall, whether pumped or drawn from surface flows.)

An earlier study by Dawson[36], designed to throw light on price elasticity of demand for water, showed as in the following table for certain other areas.

* Cents per cubic metre.

	Costs (excluding distribution) (c/m³)	Average application (metres)
Ainsworth, Nebraska	0·87	0·41
Texas High Plains	1·10	0·28
Antelope Valley, California	1·30	1·53
Eastern States	0·54	0·13

Water requirements vary of course with the extent and distribution of rainfall, and with evaporation. Climatic factors being given, Dawson estimated that price affected water use with an elasticity of about 0·5.

As stated in Chapter 1, all agricultural products will be expressed in terms of wheat. Most countries have some degree of protection for internal prices of agricultural products. When we are comparing countries with varying degrees of protection, it is convenient to work in terms of world prices, i.e. to take as our basis the price of $67 per metric ton for imported wheat at European ports in 1958–60, so that one cent can be expressed as 0·15 kg wheat. On this reckoning at world prices, for example, sugar is the equivalent of 1·27 times its weight in wheat, ginned cotton 8·65, butter 12·2. In this particular case in California, the sugar would have been sold at 50% above world prices. We can reckon that Tulare County prices on the average were 15% above world prices, i.e. we can equate one cent to 0·13 kg wheat. (In Colorado, the water was probably used to irrigate fodder crops to feed cattle which would be sold at about world price.)

An estimate of the marginal productivity of irrigation water, using production functions, was made by Hopper[37] for the village of Senapur in the Ganges Valley in India (where well water is abundant, if power is available to lift it). The marginal productivity of a cubic metre was found to be 0·25 kg wheat or 0·36 kg barley (the prices of the different crops in this area were found to be well adjusted to their marginal costs of production).

The lower of the two prices quoted as now being paid for water in West Pakistan (see the beginning of this chapter), corresponds to no more than $0 \cdot 070$ kg/m³ of wheat, $0 \cdot 072$ of maize, or $0 \cdot 049$ of rice (presumably milled), at prices prevailing there. One may perhaps expect that in the Punjab, where both geographical conditions and the availability of machinery have made water easier to obtain, marginal productivity may already be much lower than in the Ganges Valley. This is seen to be the case (Table 9). Ghulam Mohammad[34] gives the average

TABLE 9

Marginal Returns to Water in West Pakistan

	Higher rainfall area		Lower rainfall area	
	Before tube well irrigation	After tube well irrigation	Before tube well irrigation	After tube well irrigation
Areas operated (hectares)	$11 \cdot 4$	$17 \cdot 0$	$11 \cdot 4$	$22 \cdot 2$
Area cropped (hectares)	$14 \cdot 4$	$25 \cdot 7$	$11 \cdot 3$	$29 \cdot 2$
Gross product (000 rupees)	$8 \cdot 22$	$19 \cdot 68$	$6 \cdot 45$	$22 \cdot 35$
Debit fertiliser (000 rupees)	$0 \cdot 19$	$0 \cdot 76$	$0 \cdot 15$	$0 \cdot 87$
Debit labour (000 rupees)	$2 \cdot 40$	$2 \cdot 56$	$1 \cdot 60$	$2 \cdot 80$
Debit bullocks (000 rupees)	$4 \cdot 32$	$4 \cdot 96$	$3 \cdot 52$	$5 \cdot 13$
Net product (debiting above inputs only)	$1 \cdot 31$	$11 \cdot 40$	$1 \cdot 18$	$13 \cdot 55$
Tons wheat equivalent/ cropped hectare: Gross product	$1 \cdot 52$	$2 \cdot 04$	$1 \cdot 52$	$2 \cdot 04$
Net product (debiting above inputs only)	$0 \cdot 24$	$1 \cdot 18$	$0 \cdot 28$	$1 \cdot 24$

area of farms without tube well irrigation as a little over 11 hectares in both districts which he studied (Multan–Montgomery, with low rainfall and water table at $7\frac{1}{2}$ m depth, and Gujranwala–Sialkot, with higher rainfall and water table at 3 m depth). Under the conditions of the Punjab, where irrigated land can be obtained very cheaply, farmers with tube wells operated more land, and double-cropped (to the extent of 50% of their total area in the higher rainfall land and 30%

C

in the drier land), until their water supply stood at about 1 m/ year per unit of area cropped. (They probably did not need all this, and sold some to their neighbours.) Accurate information about increased yields on tube-well irrigated land is not available, and Ghulam Mohammad makes approximate estimates. He also estimates the manner in which the crop pattern is likely to be reorganised when tube-well water is available. Separate estimates are made for areas whose predominant crops are cotton and rice respectively, but the monetary results are not very different—gross returns are about 570R/hectare/year without and 765 R/hectare/year with tube-well irrigation. (It must be remembered that the land without tube well irrigation depends upon canal irrigation, but with inadequate water supply.) He finds fertiliser inputs raised from 51 to 114 kg/hectare/year of ammonium sulphate equivalents. This was available in Pakistan at a subsidised price of 130 R/ton at farm, but its true cost (judging from the experience of similarly situated countries) can be estimated at twice that. Ghulam Mohammad also gives the inputs of labour and bullock power—one of the great advantages of tube well irrigation is that it makes possible the fuller use of these resources, which were formerly under-occupied. A man's labour is valued at 400 R/year, and a pair of bullocks at 1600 R/year. Finally, rupees are converted into wheat equivalents on the local price of 375 R/ton.

If we assume that the use of tube well water averaged a depth of $0 \cdot 75$ m on all cropped land, i.e. 7500 m³/hectare, then returns measured in wheat equivalents, are seen to be $0 \cdot 125$ and $0 \cdot 128$ kg/m³ for the higher and lower rainfall areas respectively. In this area circumstances are admittedly unusual, with additional (unirrigated) land to be had cheaply. The marginal product is much below Hopper's figure, but above the price paid for water $(0 \cdot 070$ kg/m³).

However, there is more to it than that. Ghulam Mohammad writes:

> When a farmer saves or borrows 6-12000 rupees and instals a tube well his whole outlook on agriculture as a business changes. He wants to grow more valuable crops, to apply fertiliser, and to use other modern inputs to increase his income. . . . Tube wells already installed are having a powerful influence on the saving habits of neighbouring

cultivators, and most of them are planning to have their own tube wells. So far the only outlet which the farmers had for their savings was purchase of land or construction of houses. The price of (irrigated) land being extremely high, returns on investment were low and there was less incentive for saving. Now for the first time the farmers have got a low cost investment opportunity which yields extremely high returns.

Naik[38] establishes a production function with a number of variables for farms in a village near Baroda in 1960–1. Water inputs unfortunately were measured only in money and not in volume. The marginal return was $4 \cdot 8$ times the payment made for the water, which may have been anything from $0 \cdot 03$ to $0 \cdot 3$ c/m³.

These estimates based on linear programmes or production functions, which in effect allow the cultivator to change his cropping pattern as his water supply changes, give results of greater interest than simple comparisons of the unirrigated and irrigated yield of a given crop. Most of our information is in this latter form; but before we go on to examine it (Table 11) we may consider a "commonsense" programme for an Iraqi farm of 12 hectares prepared by Jewett for Hunting Technical Services.[39]

TABLE 10

Returns to Irrigation in Iraq

	Area in hectares		Crop in tons		Net return in tons wheat equivalent	
	Present	Pro-posed	Present	Pro-posed	Present	Pro-posed
Barley	4·2	2·0	4·4	2·8	1·76	1·12
Wheat	2·0	4·0	1·6	4·08	1·60	4·08
Berseem	—	3·0	(animal products)		0·82	3·17
Cotton (unginned)	0·25	1·5	0·2	1·44	0·60	4·32
Summer fodder	—	0·375	(draught animals)		—	—
Rice	0·125	0·75	0·16	1·2	0·24	1·80
Vegetables	—	0·375				1·50
Sesame	—	0·625		0·5		1·25
Total					5·00	17·24

For conversion to grain equivalents the ratio 20 dinars/ton wheat is used. At present the typical farm receives (from rainfall and irrigation) about 25 mm/month April–September, and 60 mm/month in the winter, or about 0·5 m/year; under the proposed irrigation scheme it will receive 0·96 m/year, fairly evenly distributed. The returns are calculated net of seed and other materials which have to be purchased. Labour requirements, at present 249 man-days/year, will rise to 535—no charge is made for this, as it is assumed that partially occupied labour is available. If the additional labour were charged, the rate, from experience in other low-income countries, would probably be found to be a little over 3 kg wheat/man-day or say 1 ton in all, leaving a marginal net return of 0·94 ton/ hectare or 0·20 kg/m³ of added water (1·02 tons/hectare if no charge made for labour).

We now proceed in Table 11 to a general consideration of available information on gross and net marginal returns to irrigation, expressing all products as wheat-equivalents. Net marginal return is estimated after deducting all additional costs incurred including labour, which is assumed to be available (though this is by no means always the case).

The most generous responses are shown by potatoes, in Europe as well as in U.S.A. But these are responses to comparatively small quantities of water, using costly equipment which stands idle for most of the year, on heavily fertilised crops, in the hands of exceptionally skilled growers. Similar considerations apply, though less strikingly, in explaining the high yields from tobacco, cotton and tomatoes in U.S.A., fruit, vegetables, wine and flax in France, and fruit in Italy and Australia. In the case of maize, the already high-yielding crops in U.S.A. give a much higher marginal response to water than the best French or Italian results.

Among the cereals, the high returns to wheat in France are outstanding.

In the low-income countries, the marginal returns to water also appear to be low. A well-cultivated plant of good strain seems better able to take advantage of additional water than can a poorer plant.

TABLE 11

Gross and Net Returns to Irrigation

Country	Crop or Product	Conversion Factor (kg wheat/ kg crop)	Irrigation Water Input (cm)		Gross Marginal return (kg wheat equivalent/ m³)	Net Marginal Return after meeting additional costs (kg wheat equivalent/m³)
			Specified	Not specified—approximately estimated		
Australia	Butter fat	14·7	45		0·50	
	Grass (dry weight)	0·39			0·39	
	Dried fruit				0·75	
	Canned fruit				1·85	
	Rice				0·17	
France	Flax	6·1	9·5		2·56	0·47
	Fodder crops			40	0·62	2·85
	Fruit and vegetables			40	3·55	
	Maize	0·75	25·3		0·55	
	Maize on sandy soil		24·2		1·55	
	Potato	0·65	7		11·54	
	Sugar-beet	0·15	23·3		1·14	
	Wheat	1		30	1·07	0·88
	Wine	0·85		30	2·56	1·45
India	General: Senapur					0·25
	Orissa					0·24

TABLE 11—(cont.)

Gross and Net Returns to Irrigation—(cont.)

Country	Crop or Product	Conversion Factor (kg wheat/ kg crop)	Irrigation Water Input (cm)		Gross Marginal Return (kg wheat equivalent/ m^3)	Net Marginal Return after meeting additional costs (kg wheat equivalent/m^3)
			Specified	Not specified— approximately estimated		
India (cont.)						
	Bihar					0·45
	Bombay					0·3–0·5
Iran	Wheat		220		0·045	
Iraq	Wheat		63	50	0·12	
Italy	General: Campania, 1913				1·32	
	Venetia, 1962				0·09	
	Central Italy, 1962				0·96	
	S. Italy, 1962				0·66	
	Beans	1·76			0·60	
	Cattle and mixed	2·73		50	0·15	
	Citrus (S. Italy)	0·48		25	2·03	0·12
	Grass			50		1·17
	Hay	0·24		50	0·24	0·13
	Maize (Grüner)			50	0·30	
	Maize (Cofani)	0·75		50	0·58	0·31
	Maize second crop				1·10	0·54

Italy (cont.)	Peaches				1·86	0·53
	Potatoes				5·20	0·82
	Sugar-beet	0·068			0·26	0·26
Jordan	Wheat	0·37		50	0·47	
	Wheat			50	0·23	
Lebanon	Tomato			50	0·67	0·38
New Zealand	General	0·385		50	0·27	0·08
Nigeria	Grass (dry weight)		64	50		
Pakistan	Cotton (unginned)	2·41	50		0·24	
	Rice (milled)	1·2	120		0·12	
	Sugar cane	0·13	100		0·13	
	Sorghum	0·6	20		0·08	
South Africa	Sugar cane (sucrose content)	0·92				
	Tongaat	0·92	52 66		1·10 1·40	
	Illovo	0·92	71 105		1·05 0·90	
	do. with abundant K_2O	0·92	71 105		1·29 1·08	
	Tongaat First Ratoon	0·92	36 46		1·76 1·40	
	Second Ratoon		75 84		1·32 1·48	
United Kingdom	Barley (25 kg/ha N)	0·65		10	0·24	
	Barley (50 kg/ha N)			10	0·08	
	Early potatoes	2	6		11·3	
	Sugar-beet (as sugar)	1·03	10		1·78	

TABLE 11—*(cont.)*

Gross and Net Returns to Irrigation—*(cont.)*

Country	Crop or Product	Conversion Factor (kg wheat/ kg crop)	Irrigation Water Input (cm) Specified	Irrigation Water Input (cm) Not specified— approximately estimated	Gross Marginal Return (kg wheat equivalent/ m³)	Net Marginal Return after meeting additional costs (kg wheat equivalent/m³)
U.S.A.	Butter fat (Tennessee)	14·9	53		1·06	
	Cattle liveweight: Illinois	12·1	31		0·46	
	Cattle liveweight: Georgia		20		0·54	
	Cotton ginned (Georgia)	6·5	14		2·31	
	Hay: Massachusetts	0·47	15		0·68	
	Nebraska	0·40		30	0·57	
	Maize: Georgia	0·75	18		1·68	
	Missouri		14		1·43	
	Virginia		18		2·43	
	Milk: Virginia	1·3	28		0·53	
	Potatoes: Long Island	0·65	7		5·83	
	Wisconsin		8		9·50	6·55
	Sorghum: Georgia	0·60	8		1·03	
	Soya beans: Missouri	1·3	12		1·02	
	Sweet potato: Georgia	0·3	25		1·03	
	Tobacco: Virginia	8·0	18		5·90	
	Tomatoes: Georgia	0·37	15		3·57	

Notes to Table 11

Australia

Butter fat. Reference (40). Results for Murwillumbah in the Northern Rivers district of New South Wales, where the rainfall is usually good. A time series analysis of three farms in this area over ten years (Reference (41)) suggested results about twice as high, but Waring pointed out that these advantageous marginal results were only to be obtained in the intermittent dry years. Excessive moisture, in his opinion, reduced dairy output. He also made an important point in cow psychology: "Stock allowed limited access to palatable feed at regular times will often stand waiting for long periods beforehand. There is a disinclination to forage as diligently on unattractive feed when something better is expected to be offered." He gave the expected butterfat output (1 kg butterfat makes 1·2 kg commercial butter) from sown pastures at 90 kg/hectare/year, with the possibility of raising it by 250 kg by 45 cm irrigation. Another authority (Reference (42)) claims that sprinkler irrigation can raise this yield as high as 336 kg/hectare/year of butterfat.

In estimating economic returns it must be remembered that butter in Australia sells at about 25% above world price (the coefficient of 14·7 quoted in the table is at Australian price). A more recent study by Bird and Mason[43] in the same area of the detailed accounts of fifteen farms over some years does not give the water input, which varies greatly from year to year, but assuming 43 cm average, the median gross return was found to be, in wheat equivalents, 0·41 kg/m³ (or an increment of butter fat of 145 kg/hectare, similar to the Milk Board's estimate). Additional costs however were incurred (reverting to wheat equivalent units) of 0·23 kg/m³, plus 0·13 kg/m³ cost of irrigation which leaves little net return from the operation, if butterfat is reckoned at world rather than Australian price.

Grass. Reference (44). Results for Gippsland, an area in Victoria with comparatively cool climate.

Fruit and Rice. Reference (45). Canned fruit has very considerable expenses of production to be charged against the gross return.

France

Fodder crops, fruit and vegetables, wheat, wine—Reference (46) (Lower Rhone Valley).

Flax, maize, potato, sugar beet—Reference (47). Supplementary irrigation June–September in dry years only.

Unirrigated yields tons/hectare:

Wheat	0·8	Maize	5·9
Wine	3·0	Maize, sandy soil	4·3
Flax	1·35	Potato	34·0
Fodder crops	1·2	Sugar beet	41·0
Fruit and vegetables	5·0		

India

In view of the importance of the subject to India, there has been regrettably little work done on the economics of irrigation.

Indian Statistical Institute Planning Unit, Reference (48), p. 62, gives marginal returns from irrigation for each Indian State expressed in terms of food grain equivalents. The quantities of water used are unfortunately not stated. The table is attributed to "Directorate of Economics and Statistics", but nothing is said about the methods by which the results were obtained.

A Gokhale Institute Publication, Reference (49), in 1948 reviewed eight villages in which the proportion of canal land irrigated varied from nothing to 36% (there was also some well-irrigated land, but limitations of ox-power to draw the water result in this having much less effect on productivity). These results can be—somewhat hazardously—extrapolated to estimate the gross and net marginal productivity from complete irrigation. The data are the averages for 1938–9 and 1939–40 (95 rupees = 1 ton wheat). Gross product data as given were redefined to exclude manure, seeds and fodder produced and used on the same farm, but before debiting purchases of these commodities.

In another Gokhale Institute publication, Sovani and Rath[50] estimated for Orissa, a region with a natural rainfall of 1·5 m and where therefore on the face of it there should be little need for irrigation, that irrigation could raise the proportion of land double-cropped from 22% to 67%.

Professor Gadgil[51] of this Institute in 1958 headed a group who prepared *Evaluation of the Benefits of Irrigation Projects* for Planning Commission Research Programmes Committee, examining five areas in different parts of India. The definition here of net marginal product is slightly defective in that some small payments for hired land and capital (but not imputed rent and interest on own property) have been debited (484 rupees = 1 ton wheat).

Gadgil's results were as follows (net marginal product representing the addition to factor income in the agricultural sector, after paying for all additional inputs from outside the agricultural sector, and agricultural produce used up in production; further columns then show this figure after debiting (i) hired labour, (ii) hired and family labour).

	Tons wheat equivalent/ hectare		Do. after debiting		Net marginal product indicated from difference in land prices
	Gross marginal product	Net marginal product	Hired labour	All labour	
Indian Statistical Institute					
Lowest State (Mysore)	0·42				
Median	0·62				
Highest State (Andhra Pradesh)	1·02				
Sovani and Rath, Orissa	1·63	1·18			
Gadgil, 1958					
Tribeni Canal, Bihar		2·26	2·16	2·19	0·28
Cauvery – Mettur Scheme, Madras		0·65	0·46	0·48	0·26
Damodar Valley, W. Bengal		0·16	0·05	0·02	
Gang Canal, Rajasthan		0·13	0·06	0·06	0·21
Sarda Canal, Uttar Pradesh		0·03	0·02	0·05	

	Percentage of area canal-irrigated	Tons wheat equivalent/hectare		
		Gross product	Net product	Do. less labour
Gokhale Institute 1938–40				
Four villages	0	0·40	0·31	0·07
Belpimpalgaon	7	0·35	0·28	0·05
Ozar	21	0·87	0·62	0·06
Yesgaon	31	2·34	1·54	0·58
Rahate	37	2·37	1·39	0·52

In no case do we have information on the average quantity of water supplied. If we assume this to be $\frac{1}{2}$ m, then each hectare receives 5000 m³, and Hopper's figure of $0·25$ kg/m³ would imply $1·25$ tons wheat equivalent/ hectare net marginal product. This is well above the Indian Statistical Institute estimates, of the order of magnitude of the Sovani–Rath estimate, and lies between the first and the second of Gadgil's districts in his 1958 study. The very low figures for the Sarda Canal area are explained in terms of its being easy in that area to obtain well water for land not covered by canal irrigation; the low figures for the Gang Canal and Damodar Valley are harder to explain. When the column "After debiting all labour" is higher than the previous this means that family labour input is actually reduced in the irrigation areas, and replaced by hired labour. The calculations, based on rises in land values* (lower values were shown by the Punjab Board of Economic Inquiry[52]), assume that they represent 20 years' purchase of net incomes; high rates of interest are often found in India, but these do not appear to apply in the case of land, where security is regarded as fully adequate. The low net incomes indicated may be explained by the fact that by no means all the land in the area is fully covered by canal irrigation every year.

The Gokhale Institute studies of 1938–40 show a remarkable variance within a limited area (they were confined to what was then known as Bombay Province). They show that irrigation villages which are willing and able to make large inputs of fodder, fertilisers, etc. (see differences between gross and net products) can earn high net incomes. If we extrapolate to the situation of a village where all the land is canal-irrigated, we find net products of 3-5 tons/hectare. In this region water inputs may be of the order of 1 m, implying $0·3–0·5$ kg/m³, still considerably higher than Hopper's figure.

Iran

Beckett, Reference (53). There appears to be a wastefully high input of $2·2$ m. of water. The land grows nothing without watering.

Iraq

Yudelman, Reference (54) (dry yield $0·6$ ton/hectare).

* Expected net income from land (1/20 price), rupees/hectare		
	1950–1 to 1956–7	1957–8
Old irrigated land	50	84
Bhakra Dam irrigated villages	40	43
Unirrigated land	15	23

It appears that there is some uncertainty as to whether Bhakra Dam will in fact deliver all the water expected. The irrigated-unirrigated difference of 61 rupees in 1957–8 represents $0·125$ ton wheat/hectare, and the earlier figures less than $0·1$.

Italy

Reference (55) (Italian agricultural prices at that time assumed to be 25% above world level). The irrigation season lasted for 6 months, and yield was raised from 1·05 to 9·3 tons wheat equivalent/hectare/year. Some 30–40% of the gross product was payable in rent.

Vicinelli, Reference (56), for 1962 general results. Dry yields for the three areas were 1·39, 3·85 and 1·24 tons wheat equivalent/hectare respectively. The cheapness of water in Venetia apparently causes it to be used comparatively wastefully—indeed, the yields for the three areas show a curious proportionality to the cost of the water, which is 0·31, 3·0 and 2·15 c/m³ respectively.

Grüner, Reference (28), for beans, hay, wheat and one datum for maize, pre-irrigation yields 0·8, 3·5, 0·9 and 1·5 tons/hectare respectively. Other data from Tofani, Reference (57). (The cattle and mixed farm holding of 7½ hectares had a preirrigation output of 1·47 tons/hectare gross, 1·24 net. The conversion factor here refers to cattle liveweight.)

Citrus data from Vicinelli.[56] Non-irrigated yield about 3 tons/hectare. Additional costs include 15% gross return on irrigation capital.

Data for lucerne hay supported by Merendi, Reference (58).

Received as this book was going to press was the comprehensive study by Antonietti, d'Alarmo and Vanzetti[59] (Istituto Nazionale di Economia Agraria). Tables are presented for each province showing the usual input of water for each irrigated crop, and the expected increases in yields (measured in money) and in labour requirements. Labour was costed at the average earnings prevailing in 1961 (357,000 lire/man-year in the North, 250,000 in the Centre, 184,000 in the South and 215,000 in the Islands: cost per man-day, when labour inputs were quoted in this form, taken at 1/200 of a man-year). Other deductible costs were taken at 17½% of the gross harvest (25% for orchards). All values were converted to wheat equivalents at 68,100 lire/ton.

For general arable cultivation, the median of 11 provinces showed 50 cm of water input and a net return of 0·28 kg/m³. Rice appears to be overwatered, with Lombardy and Piedmont using 3–4 m, with a net return of only about 0·1 kg/m³ wheat equivalent. Sugar-beet, in three provinces, averages 0·35 kg/m³ net return, lucerne in three provinces 0·33 kg/m³ (average watering 80 cm), grass, in five provinces, shows an average net return of 0·14 kg/m³. Excessive watering appears to be frequent here also. Tomatoes show 0·90 kg/m³ (average watering 46 cm). Vineyards in six provinces, with a median watering of only 15 cm, show a high median return of over 3 kg/m³. In Lazio spray irrigation of 7 cm yielded 4·9 kg/m³, furrow irrigation of 23 cm yielded 1·5 kg/m³. The median return from orchards in seven provinces was 0·61 kg/m³ from 20 cm watering.

Jordan

Davies, Reference (60). Dry yields wheat 0·17, tomatoes 2·97 tons/hectare.

Lebanon

Ward, Reference (61). Dry yield £L 207 (i.e. 1·22 tons wheat equivalent)/hectare. Ratio of net to gross from U.N. Relief Organization, Beirut, Reference (62), from data for Syria, where gross output is similar to that in Lebanon.

New Zealand

Woudt, Reference (63). Perennial ryegrass and clever pastures, dry yield 10·7 tons/hectare/year.

On irrigated light land farms in the Canterbury area, Stuart and Haslam, Reference (64), found, with average water input 20 cm/year, net income after debiting for management, depreciation and 6% interest on capital, of £7·3/hectare as compared with £7·8 on unirrigated. "Irrigation on these farms becomes merely a drought insurance rather than an income-earning investment", they wrote.

Nigeria

Church, Reference (65), for Niger Delta Irrigation Area. Dry yield 1·33 tons/hectare. Dry land has a labour input of 0·2 man-years/hectare and irrigated 0·31.

Pakistan

See previous tables.

South Africa

Cleasby, Reference (66). Experiments by Tongaat Sugar Company, Natal (in a high rainfall area). For plant cane water supply ranged from 1·9 to 3·1 m and for ratoon (second growth) from 1·0 to 1·9. A kilo of sugar is worth 1·27 kg wheat at world prices; the sucrose content of the cane 0·92 kg (Australian data used for milling costs).

Some interesting cross-relationships with fertiliser inputs are in progress. So far, it appears that the responses to nitrogen of ratoons are unaffected by additional water inputs.

United Kingdom

Nix, Reference (24). The results for early potatoes were only obtainable in dry years. For sugar a distribution of results was given.

Increment tons sugar/hectare	Zero or negative	Under 1·25	1·25– 2·5	2·5– 5	5– 7·5	Over 7·5
Number of cases	6	9	3	4	2	1

U.S.A.

Department of Agriculture Year Book, Reference (32). Also *Agricultural Engineering*, Reference (67), for grazing and *The Agricultural Situation*,[68] February 1953, for Nebraska lucerne.

The lands irrigated by the Columbia Basin Project in the north-west of the United States were classified[69] into 22 soil and topography types which showed a net return ranging from 1·8 c/m³, down to negative figures on very sandy soils, with a median of 0·63 c/m³. A level topography was the first desideratum. This being given, the most responsive soil types were the "Warden-Wheeler" (medium textured soil with deep uniform profiles, free of compact layers) and "Ephrata" (medium and light textured soils over porous gravels and sands, free from rocks in the plough zone).

It is interesting to summarise the highest valued returns (Table 12). The results are stated in U.S. cents, rating at world prices, where such are available (but it is necessary to use local prices, e.g. for early potatoes).

In all other cases examined, the gross return was below 10 c. The highest Indian value was 3·3 c net. Returns to irrigation water seem to follow the principle *unto everyone that hath shall be given*. High valued crops, grown by skilled specialist producers, may show very high returns per cubic metre of water (though it must be remembered that such crops may only have a limited quantity of water for a short period in each year, and that overhead costs per cubic metre may therefore be high). But irrigation yields far less return in poorer countries.

In considering the high marginal net return shown by maize growing in U.S.A. or Italy, we must remember that the circumstances are different from those in India. The maize-growing areas in U.S.A. and Italy have an adequate winter rainfall and some summer rainfall; a certain amount of additional watering at the time when the grain is forming in the middle of the summer has an exceptional marginal effect

TABLE 12

Maximum Returns to Irrigation

| | | U.S. cents/m³ of water | |
		Gross marginal returns	Net marginal returns debiting all additional costs (where available)
Potatoes	France	77	
	England (earlies)	76	
	Wisconsin	64	44
	Long Island	39	
	Italy	35	5·5
Tobacco	Virginia	39·5	
Fruit and vegetables	France	23·8	19·1
Flax	France	17·2	
Wine	France	17·2	9·7
Tomatoes	Georgia	23·9	
Cotton	Georgia	15·5	
Maize	Virginia	16·2	
	Georgia	11·3	
	Missouri	9·6	
	Italy	3·9	
	Italy second crop	7·4	3·6
Citrus	S. Italy	13·6	7·8
Fruit for canning	Australia	12·4	
Peaches	Italy	12·4	3·5

in counteracting the effects of drying winds; this applies also to wheat and cotton. Most maize growing in India is timed so that in any case this grain formation coincides with the period of heavy rainfall in the summer monsoon. It is the basic supplies of water still stored in the soil after the winter which the Indian maize grower lacks in comparison with the American or Italian. Replenishment of water supplies for maize growers by artificial means therefore should not be expected to yield so high a marginal return in India. Overfrequent cultivation in India may also lead to some loss of stored water.

In Australia, a fodder-crop irrigation project[70] costing $1 \cdot 7$ c/m³ was reckoned "not worth it at present prices". In U.S.A. the maximum which irrigators could pay has been estimated at $1 \cdot 5$–$1 \cdot 7$ c/m³[71] and at $2 \cdot 4$.[72]

If it can be shown that the costs of a particular irrigation project are in excess of the expected economic returns from it, there are many advocates of irrigation who, without seeking to exploit "public romanticism" (see Preface), or the natural tendency of politicians to like having large dams as a good subject to make speeches about, will nevertheless urge that the project be proceeded with on what they believe to be the genuine economic grounds that irrigation schemes bring in-direct economic benefits, in the form of secondary employment, and additions to public revenue, which outweigh the direct loss.

In the underdeveloped countries there may be some highly impoverished rural areas, with under-utilised resources and underemployed labour in their transport, commerce, public services, etc. If this is genuinely so, and the area in question is capable of substantially increased activities in these fields with-out having to bring in more labour and resources from outside, then we can count some "secondary economic benefit" from an irrigation scheme.

So far as the developed countries are concerned, this argu-ment may have had some validity in the 1930s when there were a great many unemployed doing nothing, and transport and other public services were obviously under-utilised. Its use today reveals a grave intellectual time-lag. In a time like the present, the economist must debit against what farmers, local traders, etc., may produce on an irrigation settlement the value of what they might have been producing without irrigation, or producing elsewhere, and only credit the net difference; and he must debit the full charges for use of transport services, etc.

This argument in its extreme form was used by the Govern-ment of Queensland, before the present writer resigned from his position as their economic adviser, who in attempting to justify a hopelessly uneconomic irrigation project, set against its annual cost (believe it or not) the expected entire gross product of the farms expected to be established, as if not only the labour and enterprise of the farmers, but also fertiliser, equipment, transport, etc., were to be had free.

One would like to be specifically reassured that such ideas are not still cherished by some Australian irrigation advocates.

CHAPTER 4

THE COSTS OF IRRIGATION

GENERAL REVIEW

The cost of irrigation water may vary greatly. Simple diversion from a flowing stream can be very cheap indeed. The need for damming increases the cost. Irrigation from wells, where subsoil water is available, is more costly. It involves the initial capital cost of digging the well* and installing a pump, and in some cases of supplying a power line to the pump. Both capital cost and operating cost primarily depend upon the depth to which the well has to be sunk.

In U.S.A. in 1939, the average costs of maintenance and operation, expressed in money of 1964 purchasing power, were $0 \cdot 16$ c/m³ delivered, or \$$13 \cdot 8$/hectare irrigated, of which 70% were interest and redemption charges on indebtedness. The average depth of water delivered was $0 \cdot 85$ m, to obtain which result, however, an average of $1 \cdot 37$ m had to enter the canals, nearly 40% being lost by seepage and evaporation. Per unit delivered, the cost was $0 \cdot 11$ c/m³ with water drawn by gravity from the natural flow of streams, $0 \cdot 33$ with water pumped from streams, and $0 \cdot 68$ for water pumped from wells. In real terms,

---

* Artesian water obtained from very deep strata, sometimes requiring pumping, but often ascending under its own pressure, found in Australia, some parts of the Sahara, and elsewhere, while of great economic value for watering livestock in otherwise arid country, has negligible economic importance for growing crops. The cost of a bore is very great, and the flow limited. After a decade or two of use, the flow tends to decline, and eventually requires pumping. But also, apart from these objections, the water is generally so highly mineralised as to make it unsuitable for growing crops on one area for long.

The persistent popular belief about "the great lake of fresh water underneath the Sahara" may, in a certain sense of the words, be geologically true, but it has no economic significance.

these costs were much the same over the whole period 1909–1949. The average lift in pumping water from wells in U.S.A. was 17 m (rather more than in India). In Italy[56] the cost of water drawn from natural streams in Venetia was 0·31 c/m³, pumped from 30 m deep wells in Southern Italy 2·15, from small dams in Central Italy 3·0. Grüner[28] gave 0·7 c/m³ for Northern Italy, 1·1 c/m³ for Catania and 3·35 c/m³ for Palermo. Costs in Israel[73] are 0·5 c/m³ for water from the Jordan, but 7·3 from springs at Tel Aviv, and estimated at 8–10 delivered to the Negev.

Costs at the low levels found in U.S.A., much of the water being derived from flowing streams, are, however, subject to diminishing returns, the more easily accessible water having been used up first. This is shown strikingly in Fig. 2.

An interesting projection[74] for costs from succeeding new dams which might be built in the Upper Missouri region shows rising marginal costs (Table 13).

TABLE 13

Marginal Costs of Water from Upper Missouri

Dependable flow (m³ × 10¹⁰/year)	Marginal costs (c/m³) for additional supply
0·25 (present supply)	
1·73	0·06
2·28	0·15
2·83	0·18
3·17	0·23
3·45	0·35
3·59	0·40
3·73	0·49

Diminishing returns, as succeeding irrigators have to make use of less naturally favoured streams and dam sites, are also found in India and Pakistan, though at a much lower cost level. For India and Pakistan (the world's principal users of irrigation water) we have abundant information about the costs at the time the works were constructed, sometimes over a hundred

IRRIGATION COSTS IN THE U.S.A.

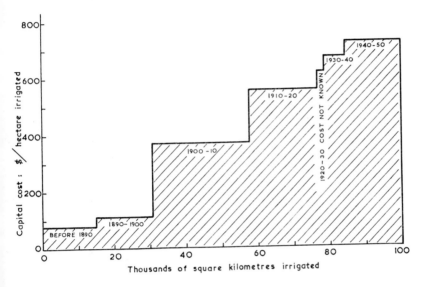

FIG. 2

years ago, and estimates of the total costs of works under construction or investigation now. All costs are expressed in our standard unit, namely a dollar of 1964 purchasing power (Table 14). The conversion of past figures to present-day costs is performed by means of index numbers whose precision is not great; but we only require orders of magnitude. In India and Pakistan most of the growth of the cultivated area over this period has been through irrigation.

Estimates[8] of water losses in transit similar to those for U.S.A. were obtained in Punjab, where it was estimated that 24% was lost in canals and distributaries and a further $21\frac{1}{2}$% in the water courses taking the water through the villages. A general figure was given of water losses at 21 cm/day per unit of water surface. Even under the driest conditions, evaporation should only account for 1 cm of the above; all the rest must be due to seepage.

TABLE 14

Dam Irrigation in India and Pakistan (excluding Burma)

Date	Total area irrigated million hectares	Specified irrigation works		
		Period of construction	Area irrigated million hectares	Average cost $ per hectare irrigated
1901	12·5	Before 1900	5·1	114
1911	17	1901–1910	1·1	87
1921	18	1911–1920	1·3	125
1931	19	1921–1930	0·75	153
1941	23	1931–1940	1·2	215
1951	29			
1955	31·5			

CAPITAL COSTS PER HECTARE IRRIGATED

At the time of the first U.S. Census of Irrigation in 1890 the average amount (in 1964 dollars) spent on irrigation had amounted to $74/hectare (though the irrigated land with its accompanying water rights then sold for $235/hectare) and the annual operating cost was $9/hectare.[75] Ideas of what constituted the economic limit for capital expenditure (measured in the same unit) were gradually rising[76] from 135 in the 1890s to 200 in 1900, 270 in 1905 and 550 in 1910—though even at that time a far higher expenditure was considered economical in Hawaii.

The average capital cost of irrigation headworks (i.e. excluding the pipes, sprays, etc., used on individual farms) is given[77] at $1250/hectare for Europe (except for Greece, where the average is only half that amount). On the new Kafue Flats project in Rhodesia the cost, including levelling, comes to $1145/hectare (converting the purchasing power of the Rhodesian £ at $4).[78] Chilean costs have been estimated[79] at $544/hectare* and the Adhaim Canal Scheme in Iraq at

---

* 20,000 pesos/hectare at 1950 prices.

$420*.[54] Various schemes in Morocco†[80] were estimated to cost $250–1600/hectare, the median (weighting by areas) being $470.

An interesting side-line on irrigation history is the canalisation of the River Swat, in the North-west Frontier Province of Pakistan, near the Afghan border, which was commenced in 1884. This was, by the standards of that time, a high-cost project, costing about $150/hectare, and deliberately undertaken by the military authorities on the grounds that the inhabitants of Swat at that time were a turbulent people who lived by raiding their neighbours, mainly because they had no alternative source of livelihood. After the construction of the irrigation canals they became a peaceful agricultural people, and Swat has remained an area of Arcadian peace and simplicity to this day.

Italian capital costs ($/hectare) were estimated as follows:[56]

Venetia (from flowing streams: largely distribution network)	560
Central Italy (of which 25% on individual farms)	750
Hill Lakes (about 200 for dam, rest for distribution)	580–770
Southern Italy (280 levelling land, 750 storage, 935 distribution, rest farm improvement)	3200‡
Spray irrigation	430

In Australia, capital costs were estimated[40] at $355/hectare for projects over 6 hectares, but at $470 for 4 hectares and $1880 for 0·4 hectare (1 acre).

Capital costs for spray irrigation in Israel were estimated[10] at $760/hectare, including well, pump, mains and sprinklers. In Egypt[10], where the Nile does most of the distributing, the cost of all irrigation work up to 1937 was estimated at only $225/hectare. The High Dam is expected to yield electricity at the rate of 10 billion kWh/year, which may have to be sold at a low price to large users. Allowing electricity sales at only 0·3 c/kWh, and capitalising at $7\frac{1}{2}$% interest rate to $40 million deduction from the total cost of $800 million, the net cost works out at $905/hectare irrigated.

---

* Excluding $28 million deficit for general river regulation.

† 1953 franc equated to 0·385 cent of 1964 purchasing power.

‡ Of which $1875 recouped as State subsidy.

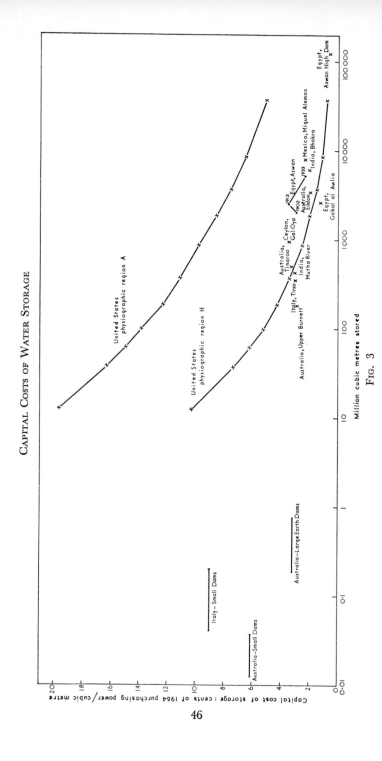

CAPITAL COSTS OF WATER STORAGE

FIG. 3

Capital cost of storage : cents of 1964 purchasing power/cubic metre

Million cubic metres stored

United States physiographic region A

United States physiographic region H

Italy – Small Dams

Australia – Small Dams

Australia – Large Earth Dams

Australia, Upper Burnett

Mutha River

India, Ingly, Tirso

Australia, Tinaroo

Ceylon, Gal Oya

Egypt, Aswan 1902

1912

1933

Australia, Eildon

India, Bhakra

Mexico, Miguel Aleman

Egypt, Gabal al Awlia

Egypt, Aswan High Dam

46

Table 15 and Fig. 3 show capital costs of various sized dams.

TABLE 15

Capital Costs of Water Storage

		Capital cost c/m³ stored	Quantity of water stored m³ × 10⁹
Australia	Eildon	2·0	3·5
	Tinaroo	3·3	0·5
	Large earth dams	3·2	
	Small dams	6·1	
Ceylon	Gal Oya	3·5	0·95
Egypt	Aswan 1902	3·0	7·0
	1912	3·6	2·5
	1933	2·3	5·2
	High Dam	0·7	18·0
	Gabal al Awla	1·3	2·6
India	Bhakra	2·0	6·1
	Mutha River	3·1	0·42
Italy	Tirso	3·0	0·35
	Small dams	9·0	
Mexico	Miguel Aleman	2·4	8·0

Notes to Table 15

Australia   *Queensland Newsletter.*[81]
            Eildon, Reference (82).
            Tinaroo, Reference (83).
            Large Earth Dams, Reference (84).
            Small Dams, Reference (44). Storage was either in gully trap
                dams or "turkey-nests" (circular dams above ground
                level).
Ceylon   International Bank, Reference (85).
Egypt   Husein, Reference (86).
            U.N. Relief and Works Agency, Reference (87).
            U.N. Economic Developments in the Middle East.[88]
            El Tonbary, Reference (89).
            Issawi, Reference (90).
            Sirry Pasha, Reference (91).
    For the first structure at Aswan (1898–1902) the original estimate was
£2 million, but additional requirements for prevention of erosion by talus
raised this to £2·72 million, for 2 billion m³ storage. Raising this to 2·5
billion m³ in 1909–12 cost £1·6 million (of which 20% was assumed to

represent compensation for land values); further additions in 1928–33 cost £2·7 million. Gabal-al-Awla (built 1933–43) cost £2·75 million. Cost of Aswan High Dam was taken at £E 180 million.

India	Gokhale Institute and Dept. of Irrigation.[15]
	The Mutha River Project was for twin earth dams about 50 m in height.
Italy	Tirso; Fortier, Reference (75).
	Small dams, Merendi, Reference (58).
Mexico	Comercio Exterior.[92]
United States	Select Committee on National Water Resources, U.S. Senate.[93]

Estimates are made for the cost of constructing water storages of given size in ten physiographic regions. Region A (the principal catchment areas in the Pacific North-West) is the most costly; Region H, covering large diverse areas all over the United States, is the lowest-cost region in which any large amount of storage is expected to be built. In Region J (Lower Mississippi) costs are 40–50% below those in Region H; but Regions I and J between them only include 3% of the water storages expected to be built in U.S.A. in the next 40 years.

It will be seen that the major dams constructed in other countries show costs comparable with those of United States Region H, and it may be deducted that these countries have not attempted to build in the physiographically less favoured areas.

Geddes,[94] *Outlook on Agriculture* (U.K.), 1964, No. 4, claims that on the Sydney University Farm at Badgery Creek costs have been greatly reduced. The first small dam of 27,000 m³ was built in 1957 at a cost of 2·5 c/m³, which cost has now been reduced to 2·1, as compared with 6·6 for the large dam at Burrinjuck, or the cost attributable to irrigation in the Snowy River Scheme.

A quite inordinately high cost of 36–72 c/m³ (£500–1000/ million gallons) was estimated[24] for small dams in England (apparently below 1000 m³). In some of these very small dams the ratio of the volume of water stored to the volume of earth excavated was not much greater than 1; no wonder the cost was high.

The Italian figures show that 5 m³ of water are stored on the average for each cubic metre of dam wall (a figure of 4 is considered to be the lower economic limit); whereas in large dams this ratio rises enormously. The figure stands at 600 in hydro-electric projects in Scotland, 1500 in the Hoover Dam, and 1,000,000 in the Owen Falls Dam in Africa.

Some interesting comparisons collected by Kanwar Sain, Director General for Irrigation in India[95] showed that, in a number of important dams in India and elsewhere, built before the 1930s, when hand labour methods predominated, the cost of the dam, per cubic metre of water stored, generally worked out at approximately 2·6 c, almost irrespective of the size of the dam. In the larger dams, a great deal more water is stored per unit volume of the dam; but the dam structure itself has to be so much more massive and costly.

"Investigation of historical data revealed no clearly established trend over time in costs per unit of capacity", wrote the U.S. Senate Select Committee. The expected rise in real costs through having used up the best sites first was about offset by declines as a result of technological advances in dam construction. They appear to be referring to the period since about 1940; previously, as we saw from the diagram in an earlier chapter, real costs were rising.

What is gained by building large water storages is however to a considerable extent lost again in the costs of the distribution network and of land levelling which are necessarily to accompany them. Thus in the Australian examples the ratio of these costs to the cost of storage was 2·15 for Tinaroo, 0·25 for the large earth dams, and nothing for spray irrigation from small dams. (Spray irrigation is comparatively costly in equipment, power and labour, but by its nature calls for no canals or ground levelling.) In South Italy the ratio was estimated at 1·25 for distribution plus 0·37 for levelling, and in Italian hill lakes at about 2·3 for distribution.[56] In India, the ratio was 0·81 for the Mutha River Project, 0·9 for Hirakud and 2·2 for Bhakra, where, for political reasons, the water had to be distributed over a much wider area than was economically justifiable.

The Indus in Pakistan has an immense summer flow from melting snows in the mountains, which is controlled by a comparatively low-cost barrage at Sukkur. In this exceptional case, the cost of canals and water courses was four times that of the barrage and headworks.

So far we have concerned ourselves with the gross costs of dams. In analysing the costs of irrigation or other water supply, however, we have to take into account the consideration that the dam may have also been built for the purpose of hydro-electric generation (dams may also serve the purpose of flood mitigation, but this is comparatively much less important, and is generally not valued). The Hirakud Dam in Orissa, an area subject to floods, was estimated[50] to have a value for flood control purposes of only 1·8 million rupees/year, which when capitalised represents less than 3% of its gross cost. The correct procedure appears to be to compute what it would have cost the authorities responsible for electrical distribution to have obtained from alternative sources, not only the same output, but also the same capacity for meeting peak demands; the meeting of such peak demands is often the most valuable function of a hydro-electric system which does not have sufficient water to run all through the year. Where a dam can supply electric power all through the year, or nearly so, it generally has to be sold at a low price to large users such as metallurgical and chemical plants which take power continuously. Thus the aluminium plant at Alwaye in Southern India in 1952 was paying only 75 rupees per kilowatt/year ($25 of present-day purchasing power, or only about 0·3 c/kWh). It was proposed that[50] the Hirakud Dam, when completed, should sell at 120 R/kW* to an aluminium plant, 210 R/kW to a ferro-manganese plant and higher to a steel plant, operating in this case at 70% load factor (i.e. power available on the average for 70% of the entire time). The above users are expected to take nearly all the power output. The Indian authorities proposed to charge 2765 R of construction cost to each kilowatt of capacity at Hirakud (465 million rupees in all); but this rate appears to be too high. A kilowatt capacity of thermal (i.e. coal or oil burning) power can now be constructed in U.S. or Western Europe for $100, i.e. 475 R at par of exchange; the median cost of thermal plants built under the Second Five Year Plan in India was 1250 R/kW.[96] We must then add the fuel savings; modern plants burn 0·45 kg coal/kW/hr, and if operating at 70% load factor such a plant would use 2·77 tons coal/kW capacity/year. If we assume that, had not the hydro-electric power been available, it would have been necessary to generate a fully equivalent amount of power thermally, this would have cost 61 R/year for fuel at Calcutta coal prices, or 100 at Bombay prices. If we capitalise these savings at 10%

* Rupees per kilowatt.

rate of interest (which rate of return on capital is easily earned in Indian industry), we obtain 600–1000 R, plus 1250 R for the generating plant and equipment. We must capitalise fuel savings at an unrealistically low rate of return on capital if we wish to reach the official valuation of 2765 R/kW for Hirakud. Moreover in this case we are considering power at a very high load factor which generally can only be used by a few specialised industries, which probably would not come into existence if cheap power were not available. Capitalising the revenue from aluminium and similar producers indicates only 1200–2000 R/kW. A load factor of 50% would be considered high in Europe, but comparatively large amounts of power could probably be sold on these terms in India, where demand has less daily and seasonal peaks; at this rate the capitalised value of the fuel saving becomes 435–715 R/year, at Calcutta and Bombay coal prices respectively.

In view of the fact that Indian thermal plant has so far been installed at anomalously high costs, which should soon be reduced, it appears sufficient to credit each kilowatt of hydro-electric power with a capital value of only 1500 R. Projects for hydro-electric generation without irrigation in the Second Five Year Plan showed a median cost of 1250 R/kW;[96] the median cost of such projects in 1949 had been 1165 R/kW,[97] equivalent to a rather higher figure by the Second Plan period.

Table 16 shows the position regarding the large dams in India, and certain others.

Some data are also available from Portugal*[99] and are shown in Table 17, omitting projects which were partly for flood prevention or drainage rather than purely for irrigation.

PUMPING—PRIMITIVE METHODS

Outstanding among the areas where irrigation can be effected by pumping water from shallow wells are the plains of India and Pakistan, through which the Ganges and the Indus river systems flow. The Punjab Board of Economic Enquiry estimated (before the Punjab was partitioned between India

* The author has been advised (private communication) that the column headed "costs" should have been headed "costs re-stated at 1955 price level".

TABLE 16

Gross Costs and Hydro-electric Credits for Large Dams

	Total capital cost million rupees	Credit for hydro-electric at 1500 R/kW million rupees	Net capital cost of irrigation rupees/hectare irrigated	Annual [a] capital charges c/m³
Bhakra-Nangal	1700	906	548	0·22
Damodar	1317	381	1727	0·69
Hirakud	933	185	1190	0·48
Chambal	620	138	1087	0·43
Tingabhadra	604	68	1600	0·64
Mayurakshi	205		708	0·28
Bhadra	335	50	2880	1·15
Kosi	448		790	0·32
Nagajunasagar	911		1095	0·44
Kakrapara	187		707	0·28
Mutha	95		3050	1·22
Pakistan: Sukkur	200[b]			0·13
Thal	350		875	0·35
Ceylon: Gal Oya	133	15	3370	1·35
Smaller dams (median)			2000	0·50

[a] Taking annual charges at 10% on capital, assuming 0·75 m average annual water application, and converting rupee at 30c (these data generally relate to a period when Indian prices were lower than in 1964).
[b] Pre-war costs.

Sources:

India — Mutha River, Gokhale Institute, private communication.[15] Others, "India 1961" (High Commissioner's Office, London).[96]
Pakistan — Department of Irrigation, private communication.[98]
Ceylon — *Economic Development of Ceylon* (International Bank), pp. 417–19.[85]

and Pakistan) that one-third of the whole area of the Province was capable of well-irrigation—subject of course, to the proviso

TABLE 17

Irrigation Projects in Portugal

Name of project	Date of completion	Area irrigated in hectares	Gross costs $/ha irrigated	Credit[a] for power generated $/ha	Net cost $ per hectare irrigated	Volume of water storage in metres average depth over area irrigated	Annual[c] capital charge c/m³
Burgaes	1940	168	1773	—	1773	0·24	2·37
Sado Valley	1949	9613	2228	137	2091	1·64	2·79
Alvega[b]	1939	422	779	—	779	—	1·04
Idanha	1954	8090	1087	94	993	0·96	1·33
Silvey	1956	1900	3800	168	3632	1·47	4·85
Campilhas	1954	1935	2840	58	2782	1·09	3·71

[a] Capacity is quoted in kWh/year (presumably because supply is intermittent). It is assumed (as in Australia) that supply is for an average of 2000 hours per year, and that the value of equipment and fuel can be capitalised at $375 per kW.

[b] Irrigation by direct pumping from river.

[c] Computed as in previous table.

that the total flow from these wells should not exceed the sub-soil replenishment, which takes place by lateral seepage from the river bed. The extent of such replenishment is not at present known, but it certainly cannot be indefinitely high—after all, the total flow through the river system is limited. Any large increase in the numbers of power-driven pumps would bring quite a rapid fall in the water table. Such a fall has been observed, for instance, in the Ayr district of Queensland, where about 15,000 hectares of sugar cane are provided with approximately $\frac{1}{2}$ m of irrigation water to secure maximum growth. This water has been obtained easily by pumping, in many cases with windmills, from wells of only about 8 m depth, which has only been in operation for a comparatively short time, but already is causing a marked fall in the water table, even for such a small area of irrigated crops.

In examining Indian and Pakistani data, we convert the rupee at 25c, as given in the Introduction, but consider costs also in grain equivalents. In many parts of the Punjab the average size of holding depends[100] on the quantity of water which two bullocks can draw from a well; which in turn depends on the level of the water-table.

Table 18[101, 102] shows the costs of various methods of raising water for a water table of 9 m depth* (it will be shown below that a greater depth probably makes irrigation economically impossible, if mechanical power is not available).

Traditional methods show a fairly low efficiency of utilisation of muscle power (a man can maintain up to $\frac{1}{2}$ h.p. in favourable circumstances and a good horse can do well over 1 h.p.). The figures also show that small pumps would be more than adequate to replace such traditional methods—even if the saving in manpower is neglected. However, there may well be a substantial saving in costs.

It might indeed be fairly easy to design a simple and very

* The data for the "well-sweep" are Dias's; the two authorities agree on the data for the "Mhote" and "Persian wheel". The area which can be watered by each device appears to have been calculated on the assumption of one metre depth and some 1800 hr/year as maximum practicable time of operation.

TABLE 18

Cost of Primitive Pumping Methods

	Required power		m³/hr delivered	Hectares watered	Capital cost c/m³ (see below)	Operating cost in c/m³ (see below)	Operating cost in kg wheat equivalent/m³ (see below)
	Men	Bullocks					
Picottah	4	—	3	0·5	0·7	3·3	0·26
Well Sweep	5	—	6	—	0·4	2·1	0·17
Mhote	2	2	7	1·2	0·3	4·3	0·35
Persian wheel	2	2	9	1·5	0·2	3·3	0·26

cheap pedal-driven Persian wheel, which would utilise human muscle power much more efficiently than the present methods. A man-hour of labour, whose present marginal productivity is 0·32 kg barley, could thereby yield 2 m³ of water[103] worth 0·72 kg barley.

For the average irrigation area we will assume a 10-hr day, with men paid 1 R/day and bullocks costing 5 R/day, and converting the rupee at 25 c, or 2 kg wheat. (At world market price, 25 c would buy 3·75 kg wheat, but the relative prices of grains, in comparison with other goods, are much higher in India than elsewhere.) The costs expressed in wheat equivalents, it will be seen, are of an order of magnitude only a little lower than the expected returns.

Hopper's work at Senapur (referred to in the previous chapter) makes the marginal value of one hour's work by a pair of bullocks, inclusive of the labour of the driver and the use of the equipment, no less than 9 times that of a man-hour. But this was in a region with a short monsoon season, during which the demand for bullock-labour for cultivation during the season was extremely urgent. A careful study in the Punjab by Shastri[105] showed that the full cost of a bullock, inclusive of interest and depreciation, was 558 R/year in 1950, or about 800 R now, and that it could usefully be used only about 160

E

days/year—even the largest farms could not get a higher utilisation than this—or 5 R per working day. At Punjab rates, this is only 3–4 times a man's wages. In West Bengal[106] where oxen appear to be abundant, and the rainy season is prolonged, so that there is less urgency about cultivation, the average agricultural wage worker is paid at the rate of $3 \cdot 5$ kg rice/day, and at only $6 \cdot 6$ if he provides the plough and a pair of oxen.

For an African family in Southern Rhodesia it is estimated[104] that a vegetable garden of 135m² is desirable. To water this at a rate of 6 mm/day during the dry season calls for lifting a ton of water a day, which is too much to attempt by hand, even if water is available in the stream-bed. From a borehole this ton (m³) of water could be supplied at $8 \cdot 8$ c (2 shillings/000 gallons). Its capacity should be 680–1360 m³/month (to supply 30–60 families), and capital cost is estimated at £600. The power in most cases would have to be diesel, as electric power lines cost £400/mile. Such costs might permit the growing of vegetables, but certainly not of staple crops.

In Southern Italy[55] in 1913 water drawn by oxen from 12-m depth wells cost $4 \cdot 7$ c/m³ (in present-day money values).

Costs of sinking wells in the Punjab[107]* at various dates in the past, expressed at present-day values, averaged $800, not varying appreciably with depth within a range 6–14 m. Assuming an 1800 hr year, no depreciation, a 5% interest rate and 9 m³/hr delivered, this imposes capital costs of $0 \cdot 25$ c/m³ (and the 5% interest rate is unrealistically low).

POWER PUMPING

We now examine the extent to which these costs can be reduced by power pumping.

In U.S.A. in 1950, as reported by U.S. Department of Agriculture, water pumped from wells was lifted on the average 30 m (considerably more than in 1939) and cost $0 \cdot 82$ c/m³, of which $0 \cdot 44$ c/m³ represented fixed charges, interest being reckoned at 5%. Assuming an average depth of watering of $0 \cdot 85$ m, and some charges for depreciation of capital as well

---

* Diameter at mouth of well averages 8 ft.

as interest, this latter figure implies an average capital cost per hectare much below that shown in Fig. 2 (lower still if we assume less than 0·85 m average depth). Many of the expensive capital works were government-provided and apparently not charged to users. The U.S. Department of Agriculture has suggested[68] that, for farmers digging their own wells in Nebraska, capital costs at the much lower figure of $270/hectare should yield a good economic result, in comparison with the alternative of buying more dry land whose price then was $370/hectare. With modern equipment, working 1000 hr or more per year, water could be pumped from a depth of 30 m (costs are approximately proportional to depth) for 0·43 c/m³, with older plant at about twice the cost.[36] It appears that most of the well irrigation recorded for 1950 was from old plant. Koenig[108] gives also 0·44 c/m³ per 30 m (100 ft) of depth, treating cost as directly proportional to depth.

Vicinelli's study for Italy showed that a 30 m lift (presumably using electric power) now cost only 0·5 c/m³, similar to the U.S. cost with new equipment.

Costs of fuel and energy—which may vary greatly between different places—represent a considerable proportion of the whole. In India and Pakistan a well depth of 12 m is usually regarded[109] as about the economic limit for depth (except for valuable crops, or for drinking water, where the limit may be 30 m). For a pump delivering 153 m³/hr (1½ cusec), a power of 10½ kW will be required. The usual formula used by engineers is that 1 m³/hr pumped from a depth of one metre requires 0·00644 kW, $\left(kW = \dfrac{\text{cusecs} \times \text{lift in feet}}{5} \right)$. In the water-logged area of Mianwali in Pakistan[110] it was planned to use 3800 kW to pump 480 million m³/year from tube wells—consistent with the above formula if average depth assumed to be 76 m. This formula would, however, be subject to wide variation according to the size of the pump; for very large pumps power requirements might be 15% less, for very small ones well over 50% more. This formula assumes that the pumps are run under their designed condition; the efficiency will fall fairly rapidly if the head flow or speed are altered.[103]

The pump of 153 m³/hr capacity considered above, at 12 m depth of water table (the maximum possible depth for a masonry well; to go deeper a metal-lined tube-well is required), may be expected[109] to work 3000 hr/year and will be able to water 72 hectares to an average depth of 0·64 m, and will use 91,000 kWh of power or 0·08 kWh/m³ water; and for deeper wells these requirements will increase in direct proportion. At its very cheapest, near to a big hydro-electric plant, this amount of power might cost only 0·03 c/m³; at U.S. bulk prices, about 0·09 c/m³; under less favourable circumstances twice that or more. On Ghulam Mohammad's cost figures for Pakistan, power costs 0·08 R/kWh, or 2 c at our purchasing parity rate of exchange, i.e. 0·16 c/m³. For a diesel pump of 102 m³/hr costs of fuel and lubricant are 0·22 c/m³, at Pakistan prices—only 0·12 at U.S. diesel oil prices.

In Israel[111] where pumping is probably from much deeper wells, a cubic metre of water requires 0·25 kg of fuel, or over 0·54 c/m³; in Australia[44] the fuel costs work out at 0·43 for diesel and 0·79 for electricity. Fuel costs[112]* in U.S. (assuming that maize and cotton received 0·3 m of artificial watering, pasture 0·5) also work out at 0·47 c/m³; presumably the water had to be obtained from a considerable depth. The proposition that costs are proportional to depth is only true in a general sense, and if different sized pumps are used for different wells. For a pump of given size there comes a depth beyond which water can only be obtained at inordinate costs.

Ghulam Mohammad[34] gives (Table 19) figures of output and total costs, charging 8% on capital, and full depreciation. Fuel costs are distinguished (with electric power at 0·08 R/kWh, diesel fuel at 0·36 R/l.). Rupees are converted at $0·25.

From the engineer's point of view, costs can be brought to near the minimum by pumps of 5 cusecs (510 m³/hr)—if it is possible to dispose of the water economically. In general, a diesel pump will use about 0·45 kg(0·53 l.)/h.p./hr. The capital cost of an electric pump will be about $80/kW—to which must be added the cost of the well and of the electrical connection.

Some estimates[101, 113] are available for fuel costs and capacities of given pumps at varying depths (Table 20). Fuel requirements are as given by Tainsh, given by volume and

---

* Labour costs estimated at $0·5 per hour were raised to $0·75 to accord with the average for U.S. (1950).

TABLE 19

Irrigation Costs in W. Pakistan

	Output 000 m³/ year	Capital cost 000 R	Total annual cost c/m³	Of which fuel c/m³
Gujranwala-Sialkot area (higher rainfall, water table depth about 3m):				
Electric pump	236	5·4	0·29	0·17
Diesel pump.	304	8·5	0·39	0·20
Multan-Montgomery area (low rainfall, water table depth about 7½m):				
Electric pump	266	8·8	0·37	0·20
Diesel pump	317	12·0	0·49	0·25

(Pumping averaged 2350 hr/year in 1963/4, at 115 m³/hr.)

TABLE 20

Costs of Pumping at Various Depths

Depth in metres	Larger pump		Smaller pump	
	Capacity m³/hr	Fuel costs c/m³	Capacity m³/hr	Fuel costs c/m³
6	204	0·10	128	0·08
8	183	0·11	99	0·10
10	165	0·12	90	0·11
12	153	0·13	78	0·13
14	126	0·16	66	0·15
16	102	0·19	51	0·19
18	72	0·27	33	0·30
20	36	0·55	9	1·10

converted to money at the U.S. farmers' price of 4·34 c/l. of diesel fuel. They exceed the engineer's ideal of oil fuel requirements of 1 lb/h.p./hr by 30% at 12 m, and more at other depths.

The size of the pump needs to be adapted to the depth at which it is to work, and beyond certain limits only very large pumps are feasible (see Appendix).

Naylor[30] found in the Khairpur area of W. Pakistan that a large tube well of $2 \cdot 7$ million m³/year capacity, working 70% of the time at a depth of 60 m, cost $0 \cdot 8$ to $1 \cdot 1$ c/m³. This cost includes interest and depreciation on the electric power provision (capital cost $3 \cdot 75$ c/m³/year, including cost of power supply). But this is for exceptionally deep wells planned to drain land which has become gravely waterlogged. Tube wells for irrigation in India, where electric power is already available, have much lower capital and operating costs. In the Gorakhpur area[114] capital costs are estimated at only about 1 c/m³/year and operating costs including power, assuming average irrigation depth of $0 \cdot 64$ m, only $0 \cdot 15$ c/m³.

This may, however, have been an exceptionally favoured area. On 380,000 hectares watered by tube wells in the United Provinces in India in the 1930s capital costs[115] worked out at $1 \cdot 7$ c/m³/year in present-day values. In the case which we have observed above of a 12 kW pump watering 72 hectares, capital cost[116] will be only $4/hectare for the pump and motor. The capital cost attributable to 12 kW power capacity, plus distribution lines, is about 12,000 R, or another $0 \cdot 65$ c/m³/year. Allowing 20% for interest and depreciation, capital charges are $0 \cdot 16$ c/m³.

It will be a matter of great interest, however, for India and Pakistan if new low fuel, capital and maintenance costs are found to be possible for a new type of heat engine which burns oil and vaporises, not water, but fluids of high molecular weight, and which has the great advantage that it can be completely sealed, and should only need inspection and maintenance at long intervals.

Original work on small turbines using organic working fluids was done by Tabor and Bronicki of the Israeli National Physical Laboratory in connection with the development of a solar power unit.[117] Wilson (Oxford University Department of Engineering Science) and Moss (Esso Research) are trying to develop a cheap and efficient oil-fired version of this machine.

Ghulam Mohammad's full costs (converting at $0 \cdot 25$/R) are given in Table 21 for pumps working 275 days of 8 hr each year.

Under Pakistan conditions, the rate of interest should be at least doubled. The depth of the wells is not stated, but is apparently at about the 12 m which he regards as the economic

TABLE 21

Comparison of Diesel and Electrical Pumping Costs

Capacity m³/hr	Diesel 102 (1 cusec)	Electric 127 (1¼ cusec)
Costs (c/m³)		
Interest at 4%	0·06	0·03
Depreciation at 10%	0·16	0·07
Oil and lubricant	0·22	—
Electric power	—	0·22
Wages (operation and maintenance)	0·10	0·06
	0·54	0·38

limit. The diesel pump has higher capital charges (if it is not debited with the capital cost of electric power generation and distribution) and also requires more skilled maintenance. Capital costs for the wells and pumps alone appear to have been R14,400 for the diesel and R7800 for the electrical system of 25% higher capacity. Large numbers of private tube wells are now being constructed in Pakistan, at very low costs. Government projects are much more expensive—this is partly but apparently not entirely accounted for by their being deeper. There appear also to be substantial diseconomies of scale— well, power line and drainage all cost more per m³/hr as the project is enlarged. Projects for pumping 400 m³/hr had a capital cost per m³/hr about seven times as great as the small electric pump costed above. This is one of the most interesting and important features of the economics of irrigation.

A large-scale enquiry[12] by the U.S. Government on Pakistan's behalf estimated capital requirements per unit of area, which can be re-expressed per m³ on the basis of the average annual depth of watering of 0·64 m (Table 22).

To the above capital costs ($153/hectare) they proposed to add $30/hectare for production and distribution of nitrogen fertiliser, $5/hectare for pest control and $12/hectare for education.

Other capital costs may be expressed in the same units of c/m³/year on the assumption of an average annual watering of 0·64 m.

TABLE 22

Estimate of Capital and Operating Costs for Pakistan

Capital costs in c/m³/year			
Wells, power lines and substations	1·59	Annual costs (including interest but not amortisation)	0·33 c/m³
Drainage	0·19		
Channels for "exporting salt"	0·25		
Canal enlargement and improvement	0·36		
	2·39		

Net marginal returns to the use of water in India (see previous chapter) have been variously estimated, but may be as low as 0·25 kg wheat equivalent, i.e. 1·7 c/m³ at world prices, or more than twice that at Indian grain prices. Even at world prices this shows a wide margin of return over pumping costs, even from wells 60 m deep. The man and ox-powered pumps, on the other hand, are only doubtfully worth while at Indian prices at a depth of 9 m.

Even though we are not told what was the amount of water delivered per hour, it is interesting to know[118] that a power-pump in a village in Vietnam is leased at the high rate in terms of milled rice (more valuable than wheat) of 19 kg/hr. If we assume the depth of the water table at 9 m the pump may have delivered a little below 100 m³/hr, and it appears that the owner was charging the full marginal value of the water, which we may put in terms of milled rice at 0·2 kg/m³.

In U.S.A., where pumping costs are lower, the economic limits have been estimated[119] at 15–22 m depth for watering lucerne (alfalfa) and as much as 90 m for citrus.

For Italy, Grüner[28] considered 1·7—2·3 c/m³ as the economic limit of cost for the use of irrigation water, thus ruling out ox-powered pumping, and also a number of other schemes now in operation.

In Australia, Waring[40] had estimated 1·3 Australian pence/m³ (1·22 c/m³) as the cost of irrigating pastures, but estimated that this was above the economic limit, on the grounds that the same gross marginal yield of butterfat could have been obtained by spending 1·08 pence on purchasing 0·17 kg starch equivalent in the form of sorghum. This latter calculation however was based on the assumption of a marginal return of 0·2 kg butterfat/kg starch equivalent. Experiments have shown, however, that even the best cows have a marginal return to feeding with grains only about one-third of this. At Australian prices of butterfat the economic limit to the cost of irrigation water might be as high as 3 c/m³.

Table 24 gives estimates of total cost in c/m³ of irrigation water delivered (sources as quoted above for capital costs, unless otherwise indicated).

We have hitherto been dealing with the costs of large quantities of water distributed through furrows. Where smaller quantities of water have to be distributed to valuable crops (e.g. potatoes, tobacco) in a comparatively short time, spray distribution is necessary, at considerable increased cost per m³.

For United States[120] a detailed comparison of furrow and sprinkler costs is available (Table 23):*

TABLE 23

Furrow and Sprinkler Costs (c/m³)

		Sprinkler	Furrow
Fixed costs:	Depreciation	0·25	0·09
	Interest	0·11	0·17
	Taxes and insurance	0·04	0·04
Variable costs:	Water charges	0·21	0·21
	Labour	0·35	0·25
	Power	0·18	—
	Maintenance	0·09	0·18
	Total	1·24	1·02

* Estimates for a 24 hectare farm receiving 71 cm in 7 applications (every 2 weeks in summer). However, Wright Rain (private communication) found in the Sena Sugar Estates in Mozambique that furrow irrigation called for higher capital investment than spray and used 25% more water to attain the same result.

Table 24

General Review of Costs (c/m³)

Australia	Waring, spray irrigation	$1 \cdot 6$—$3 \cdot 0$[a]
Australia	A.B. Ritchie[70], Penshurst, Victoria	$1 \cdot 7$[b]
Australia	Mareeba-Dimbulah Scheme[6]	$6 \cdot 3$[c]
Iran	Qanats[53]	$0 \cdot 16$[d]
Israel	Spray irrigation	$3 \cdot 4$
Italy	Venetia, from streams	$0 \cdot 3$[e]
	Central Italy	$3 \cdot 0$
	Southern Italy	$2 \cdot 15$[f]
	Spray irrigation, plains	$2 \cdot 5$
	Spray irrigation, hilly country[58]	$9 \cdot 0$
United Kingdom	Sewage effluent [121]	$2 \cdot 0$[g]
	Farm irrigation[122] including costs of well or dam	$11 \cdot 3$
	Do. from streams, below 10,000 m³	$11 \cdot 7$
	Do. from streams 10,000–140,000 m³	$6 \cdot 4$

[a] Labour requirements $\frac{1}{2}$ to 1 man-hour per acre-inch (103 m³) representing 25–30% of total cost. Capital charges, including depreciation and maintenance, computed at $11\frac{1}{2}$%.

[b] Plan for irrigating 70 hectares (i.e. enough to keep one man fully occupied) using both dam and well water. Cost of equipment (i.e. excluding dam and wells) $400/hectare of which 100 electrical (power cost $1 \cdot 1$ c/kWh). 20% of total cost is for 500 hr of managerial supervision, costed at £1/hr.

[c] Capital costs were 117 c/m³—probably a world record.

[d] Water supply is obtained from *Qanats*, or nearly horizontal adits to aquiferous rock in the hills. Currency is converted on the price of wheat in 1950: 400 tomans = 1 ton wheat = $67. Capital cost of water supply is $1 \cdot 51$ c/m³ of capacity, and the owner's charges are at the rate of $\frac{1}{2}$% for maintenance plus 10% net return. This cheap water is wastefully used.

[e] An early study (International Institute of Agriculture, June 1913) gave a similar cost in Venetia, and for Southern Italy (Campania) $5 \cdot 3$, of which $4 \cdot 65$ was the cost of an ox-lift of 12 m.

[f] Includes $0 \cdot 5$ cost of pumping for 30 m.

[g] For a large pump of 638 m³/hr, costing £2200, assumed 10% capital charges and 2000 hr/year utilisation (i.e. $0 \cdot 06$ c/m³). Power costs $1 \cdot 33$ c/m³ and labour $0 \cdot 60$ c/m³.

Official estimates[93] suggest that additional water could be obtained by damming the Upper Missouri to the extent of $3 \cdot 4$ million m³/day at a bulk cost of only $0 \cdot 4$ c/m³. But, at the other end of the scale, in the Rio Grande – Pecos region, where present storage is $7 \cdot 3$ billion m³ and it is proposed to raise it to $9 \cdot 1$, annual capital charges will rise from $8 \cdot 1$ million to $12 \cdot 9$ million, for a not greatly increased flow (14 million m³/year) representing a marginal cost of no less than 35 c/m³. At this rate, the committee points out, all irrigated agriculture in this region will have to be abandoned—and perhaps some urban settlements too.

Water from the immense new Feather River project in California[123] will cost $6 \cdot 5$ c/m³ at 5% interest. At the rate actually paid by the State $(2 \cdot 7\%)$ the cost falls to $4 \cdot 1$, on a total capital cost of $1 \cdot 5$ billion. It appears that costs in California have been rising very rapidly since the best dam sites have been used up. In 1925, a transition period, costs[75] in c/m³ were $0 \cdot 7$ for the public utilities and $0 \cdot 8$ for the old established irrigation districts, and $1 \cdot 2$ for the Sacramento and San Joaquin schemes, but had already risen to $1 \cdot 7$ for some Mutual Water Companies and to $3 \cdot 8$ for the Santa Clara scheme.

CHAPTER 5

WATER RESOURCES

IT IS fitting that an examination of the problem of water resources should begin with the global review of a French writer,[124] who summarised the water resources of the world, which contains $1 \cdot 35 \times 10^{18}$ m³ in the oceans, another 4% (enough to raise the level of the sea appreciably if they melted) or 5×10^{16} m³ in the polar ice caps, 4×10^{14} m³ in the world's rivers and lakes, and 3×10^{14} m³ in artesian basins. Rainfall is 4×10^{14} m³/year of which, however, three-quarters falls directly back into the oceans. Of the rainfall on land one-quarter reaches the sea in rivers, the remainder being evaporated from soil, vegetation or water surfaces. Even so, this river flow now reaching the sea represents an annual average of over 8000 m³ per head of the world's present population.

In recent years many (though not all) of the principal countries using irrigation have shown a substantial increase in areas irrigated (see Table 26). A world total for the 1930s was estimated by Pearson and Harper at Cornell (Table 25)[125] and more recent data are given by F.A.O. (Table 26).

TABLE 25

Irrigated Area in 1930s

Continent	Total food crops	Irrigated area, millions of hectares
Asia	192	57
Europe	192	6
North America	128	11
Africa	61	4
South America	33	3
Oceania	10	0·5
World	619	81

Table 26 (for Notes see next page)

Irrigated arable land (excluding pastures)

	000 hectares (FAO Production Yearbook data)	
	1949	1962 (or most recent figure)
Europe:		
Italy[a]	129	119
Portugal[a]	28	37
Spain	1257	2029
Yugoslavia	65[b]	139
North and Central America:		
Canada		346[c]
Mexico	2919	4250[c]
Puerto Rico	26	39
United States	10721[e]	11257[i]
South America:		
Argentine	1000[d]	1500[g]
Chile	1300[e]	1363[g]
Colombia		505[f]
Asia:		
Ceylon	223[d]	368
China (Taiwan)	493[e]	492
India	19029	24362[h]
Iran	1600[e]	4651[c]
Iraq	1250[e]	3675[i]
Israel	41[j]	141
Japan	2794[a]	3369[c]
Lebanon	30	72
Malaya	150	221
Pakistan	8684	11070[g]
Philippines	516	808[c]
Syria	395[e]	558[h]
Thailand	601[d]	1878
Turkey	80[e]	1988[g]
Africa:		
Egypt	2445	2481[h]
Madagascar	263	610[h]
South Africa	405	607
Sudan		790[c]
Southern Rhodesia	6	23
Oceania:		
Australia[k]	317	1001
New Zealand	3	77[h]

Notes to Table 26

  (a) Arable refers to rice only.
  (b) 1954.
  (c) 1960.
  (d) 1948.
  (e) 1950.
  (f) 1956.
  (g) 1957.
  (h) 1961.
  (i) 1959.
  (j) 1951.
  (k) Including cultivated grassland.

TABLE 27

Water Requirements in France

	"Units"
Domestic	0·19[a]
Industry: Gross including re-circulation	1·04
Net	0·65
Irrigation	1·0
Navigation	0·13

[a] Per head of population this amounts to 120 l./day or 27 imperial gallons.

To irrigate a million hectares to a depth of 1 m annually requires a water supply of 10^{10} m³/year. In the data on water resources which follow this amount will be designated as a "unit".

We may begin by examining water requirements in countries where irrigation does not play a major part. For France[124] in 1955 the estimated requirements of a population of 43 millions are shown in Table 27. The large figures given for irrigation cannot possible be reconciled with only 30,000 hectares land reported irrigated, and may be an error.

In general, supplies are abundant. But the densely populated Lille–Roubaix–Tourcoing area of 62 km² has an average rainfall of 0·74 m, of which 0·31 m reaches the water table.

Present drawings* exceed this by 10%, or 3 cm of water annually, and the water table has been falling on the average 26 cm/year since 1921 (about what was to be expected, as the average water content of saturated soil is some 12% by volume).

For West Germany a detailed flow diagram is available. For a 1957 population of $51\frac{1}{2}$ millions, considerably concentrated in a limited area along the Ruhr, where they have to use water economically, requirements were as shown in Table 28.

TABLE 28

Water Requirements in West Germany

	"Units"
Domestic	0·22
Irrigation	0·20
Industrial	0·76
(of which used only for cooling, and directly re-usable)	0·38
Treated water (besides cooling water) returned to circulation	0·36

Sewage discharged untreated was only 0·1 (much lower than in France) and industrial wastes discharged untreated 0·06 units.

Israel and U.S.A. are countries where a high proportion of all water use is for irrigation.

An estimate[73] for Israel puts agricultural annual use at 0·1 units (i.e. an average depth of about $\frac{2}{3}$ m on 150,000 hectares, as against only 30,000 hectares irrigated in 1949), greatly overshadowing 0·025 domestic and 0·006 industrial use. The new scheme for irrigating the Negev from the Jordan

---

* Per head consumption of domestic plus net industrial water in this area drawn directly from streams is about 10% above the national average.

will ultimately use 320 million m³/year. This will reach the limit of potential yields which are put at:

Jordan	0·08
Springs	0·043
Ground water	0·065
Storm water, reclaimed wastes, etc.	0·022
	0·18 units

The official estimates and projection[93] for United States are shown in Table 29.

Gross industrial use in 1953 was stated[126] to include (in the same units) 1·7 for iron and steel, 0·7 for oil refining, 0·5 for paper and pulp, 0·1 for synthetic rubber, and only 1·3 for all other industry. This concentration of demand in three industries is striking.

The principal demand for water is for the dilution of domestic and industrial effluents to a level which the dweller further downstream will tolerate. Contamination can be measured (apart from the effects of some particularly toxic industrial wastes) by biochemical oxygen demand. The standard here adopted is the preservation of oxygen to the extent of 4 mg/l. As we become more fastidious about the amount of dirt and smell and destruction of fish life which we will tolerate in our rivers, the greater the amount of water which we will require for diluting wastes, other things being equal. Measured net the requirements of agriculture are seen to be very large in relation to all other uses. If, however, we were willing to spend more on the treatment of effluents, the volume of water needed to dilute them to a tolerable level would be less. The time may come (to use Professor Isaac's admirable phrase) when we will decide that we can no longer afford to use a thousand tons of water to carry away one ton of waste.

In face of these expected demands, rising to 96·6 units by the end of the century, the average flow of all streams in U.S. was estimated in the Paley Report on Natural Resources (1952) at 187 units, nearly twice the end-century demand—though

TABLE 29

Water Requirements in U.S.A.

	Units					
	1954		1980		2000	
	Gross	Net[a]	Gross	Net[a]	Gross	Net[a]
Agriculture	24·2	14·3	23·0	14·4	25·4	17·4
Power stations (cooling)	10·2	0·1	35·6	0·2	59·1	0·4
Manufacture and mining	4·6	0·4	14·4	1·3	32·0	3·0
Domestic and other	2·3	0·3	3·9	0·5	5·8	0·8
Increased requirements for lakes				9·8		13·4
Required for dilution of effluents		70·7		46·0		61·6
Required minimum drawings upon stream flow (sum of above)		85·8		72·2		96·6
Additional requirements to be provided if possible:						
Hydro-electric		51·9		85·3		88·0
Navigation		38·8		32·9		30·5
Fishing		10·8		23·6		33·3
Population (millions)		162		244		329

(a) After allowing for water returned to streams.

the stream flow is very irregular between seasons, and large costs have to be incurred for storage if the total flow, or indeed any large fraction of it, is to be utilised.

If enough water can be stored on the one hand, and economised by better treatment of waste, or reduction of excessive irrigation demand on the other hand, there are further claimants for large quantities of water, in hydro-electric generation, navigation, and the improvement of fishing.

In the western states of U.S.A. it is estimated[127] that water supply available for irrigation averages 48 units annually, of which 9·6 are at present used to irrigate 10 million hectares (i.e. average supply, before losses in transit, about 1 metre). These ideas seem to conflict with the official estimate. The maximum use is put at 16 units to irrigate 17 million hectares.

The data for India are given in Table 30.

F

TABLE 30

Present and Potential Utilisation of Indian Rivers[97]

	Area million hectares	Average rainfall (metres)	Average run-off (metres)	Stream flow units	Present use for irrigation units	Proposed use for irrigation and power units	Land irrigated million hectares[a]	
							Present	Proposed
West Coast river basins, excluding Indus	49·2	1·22	0·63	31·0	1·4	5·1	1·2	2·2
Indus Basin (excluding W. Pakistan)	35·4	0·56	0·22	8·0	1·3	3·0	1·6	4·3
East Coast river basins, excluding Ganges and Brahmaputra	119·0	1·09	0·34	41·2	3·0	16·1	7·5	12·1
Ganges Basin (excluding E. Pakistan)	97·7	1·11	0·50	49·0	3·2	6·1	7·8	11·8
Brahmaputra Basin (excluding E. Pakistan)	50·6	1·22	0·75	38·2	0·4	4·4	0·4	0·4
Rajputana (draining inland)	17·0	0·29	0	0	0	0	0·5	0·5
All India	365·9	1·06	0·45	167·4	9·3	34·7	19·0	31·3

[a] A unit is 10^{10} m³/year, required to irrigate a million hectares to the depth of 1 m.

The average rainfall in India is quite high, but it will be seen that a great deal of it evaporates before it reaches the river bed. And the evaporation is generally highest where the rainfall is least.

On the east coast, below the Ganges Valley, it is hoped to conserve 40% of the stream flow, as against 8% at the present time. In the more humid Ganges and Brahmaputra Basin it is not proposed, in the present system of river plans, to attempt to conserve more than 20% of the flow.

The Brahmaputra conservation will be entirely for hydro-electric power—in that district any water required for agriculture can be readily obtained from wells or ponds.

Geographers have tried out a large number of formulae to express run-off as a function of rainfall under different circumstances. Khosla (Chairman of the Water Irrigation and Navigation Commission) advanced, under Indian conditions, a very simple formula which is found to fit the facts adequately. If rainfall and run-off are both expressed in centimetres, then the difference between them, or evaporation, in any district, also expressed in centimetres, is determined by taking the average temperature in Centigrade, and dividing by $2 \cdot 07$. (This relationship does not hold for temperatures below $4 \cdot 6 \,°C$—temperatures which are very rarely experienced in India).

A formula for low rainfall countries, developed in Tunis by Tixeront[128] is as follows:

$$\text{Run-off in metres} = A \,(\text{rainfall in metres})^3$$

where for Tunis A lies between $0 \cdot 25$ and $0 \cdot 4$. Data for Australian[129] rivers also indicate a cubic relationship with a coefficient of $0 \cdot 2$. Roederer's data for Morocco[130] also show something like a cubic relationship, with the constant at $0 \cdot 22$ for the Atlantic coastal rivers, $0 \cdot 35$ for rivers of the Rif, and about 1 for the Saharan rivers of the Atlantic–Atlas slope. For the latter however a better fit is obtained with an exponent of 2 and a coefficient of about $0 \cdot 7$.

Data for Ceylon[85] appear to indicate a value of A of $0 \cdot 15$–$0 \cdot 2$ and an exponent of 2 instead of 3. The fact that the high lands, unlike those of India or Tunis, are covered with dense jungle, may increase transpiration and reduce run-off.

On the other hand, the increased evapotranspiration due to

tree cover must not be exaggerated. Recent measurements in the Hartz Mountains[131] showed evapotranspiration of $0 \cdot 58$ m/year by trees and $0 \cdot 52$ by grass nearby (out of rainfalls of $1 \cdot 25$ and $1 \cdot 22$ respectively).

Under Australian conditions,[132] where rainfall is irregular and the ratio of stream run-off to rainfall low, it is estimated that 20% of the flow of a river is generally the maximum utilisable proportion, and that the present irrigated crop area could be extended at most two- or three-fold, and even then at considerable cost. In Taiwan[133] a dense population drawing water for rice growing diverts $1 \cdot 02$ units in an average year and lets $3 \cdot 02$ units flow into the sea (total rainfall on the island $8 \cdot 88$ units).

The total flow of the Indus is $20 \cdot 7 \times 10^{10}$ m³/year (9% originating in Afghanistan, 14% in Tibet, 17% in Pakistan and the rest in India). In 1954 India used $1 \cdot 1$ and Pakistan $8 \cdot 2 \times 10^{10}$ m³/year; after some exchanges and extensions, under the Indo-Pakistan agreement sponsored by the World Bank, the final figures are expected to become $4 \cdot 1$ and $10 \cdot 9$ respectively, leaving only 28% of the flow to run to waste instead of 55% as it then was.[134] By 1964 the proportion unused had fallen to 36%[109]

The extreme variability of the flow is shown by the following figures[98] (Table 31, 1921–51 average) of stream-flow entering the Pakistan province of Punjab, and 1932–40 data of utilisation of Indus waters in Punjab, and the down-stream province of Sind.[116] In considering these latter figures, it must be borne in mind that lower down the stream the Indus will have absorbed other rivers as tributaries and also to some degree regularised its flow. Data are expressed in units of 10^{10} m³/month, so that they can be added to give the annual flow.

In Pakistan records, the season October–March is called "Rabi" and the season April–September, when the river rises with the melting snows, "Kharif".

The total flow of the Nile is 83 billion m³, of which 48 are already used in Egypt, to irrigate $2 \cdot 5$ million hectares, or $2 \cdot 9$ million if we allow for double cropping, to an average depth of some $1 \cdot 7$ m, and another 4 in Sudan.

The Sudan[135] at present irrigates $0 \cdot 4$ million hectares of the Gezira Scheme by stream flow. A total of $1 \cdot 26$ million hectares

TABLE 31

Indus flows

	Minimum monthly flow		Maximum monthly flow		Indus average flow		
	All rivers	Indus	All rivers	Indus	Used in Punjab	Used in Sind	Unused
January	0·3	0·2	0·7	0·3	0·18	0·14	0·10
February	0·3	0·2	0·8	0·3	0·21	0·15	0·07
March	0·4	0·2	1·4	0·5	0·27	0·11	0·16
April	0·6	0·3	1·7	0·8	0·28	0·12	0·37
May	0·8	0·4	3·3	1·8	0·46	0·20	0·64
June	1·7	1·1	4·5	2·7	0·66	0·44	1·37
July	2·8	1·7	6·9	4·1	0·70	0·64	1·96
August	2·6	1·5	6·7	3·4	0·90	0·76	2·35
September	1·2	0·7	3·5	1·4	0·67	0·44	1·38
October	0·5	0·3	1·1	0·5	0·41	0·23	0·34
November	0·3	0·2	0·6	0·3	0·24	0·17	0·16
December	0·3	0·2	0·6	0·3	0·18	0·09	0·15

irrigated by pumping and 0·57 by pumping is proposed. To supply this area, Sudan proposed to abrogate the 1929 agreement with Egypt and to build a dam of 3 billion m³ for the Managil Scheme at Dumazin Rapids (three times the size of Sennar).

The new Aswan High Dam is expected to make another 12 billion m³ available for irrigation in Egypt,[86] and to make a net reduction of 2·2 units in the amount of water flowing to the sea, a substantial part of which will be retained in Sudan.[136] The Egypt–Sudan Nile Waters agreement of 1929 provided that during the period 1 January—15 July, during which the total flow averaged only 15·4 billion m³, Sudan should only take 1·47 billion. During the rest of the year Sudan was permitted to take up to 14 million m³/day into the Gezira canals, fill the Sennar Reservoir (1·93 billion m³), flood certain basin-irrigation lands, and water 189,000 hectares at the rate of 7 mm/day. These rights used to the limit would add up to some 8 billion m³ for the season; Sudan in fact has only been

TABLE 32

Potential Irrigation in Middle East

Country	Cultivated	Total cultivable	Irrigated	Irrigable
		000 hectares		
Lebanon	350	500	40	200
Syria	2000	4000	240	1300[c]
Jordan	450	600	26	32
Turkey	14,300	50,000	40	300
Iraq[a]	2700	9100	2500	4500
Iran	10,000	50,000	2000	6000
Egypt	2200	3200	2200	3200
Israel	190	890	20	220[b]
Total	32,190	118,290	7066	15,752

[a] Alternative estimates by Powers (*Geographical Review*, July 1954) show 4·9 million hectares irrigable, 2·8 now irrigated (often very partially). Powers estimates total stream flow at 6·5 units/year, as against Bonné's 6·2 and points out that as the maximum rate of flow is 5½ times the average, it is unlikely that the 3–4 units/year of water, which Bonné hopes will be available to irrigate 4½ million hectares, will in fact be available.

F.A.O. Middle East Development Project, however, also consider that 3·65 units will be available (i.e. sufficient to water 3·65 million hectares to a depth of 1 m) even though they estimate the average flow of the Tigris at Baghdad at 3·9 of which 1·6 from the Euphrates. The amount available for irrigation used to be only 0·61, but, since flood control has been undertaken, has been 1·37, of which 0·32 from Euphrates.

[b] Assuming an average requirement of water (at stream bed) of somewhat over a metre, this estimate is confirmed by Blass (*Water Resources of Israel*) who states the sources of the water as follows ($m^3 \times 10^7$): Upper Jordan 70–75, Yarkon 24–25, Springs 22–27, Flood flow 19–34, Underground water 96–132, Total 231–293.

[c] United Nations Relief Agency (*Quarterly Bulletin*, March 1958) give an estimate of 1,000,000 (of which 300,000 from the Euphrates and Orontas) as against the Syrian Government's estimate of 750,000.

taking about 4 (Egypt taking 30). Under the new agreement of 1959 Egypt is to take 55½ billion m³/year and Sudan 18½ (of which 28 and 2 respectively will be in January–July period).[90]

Central Asia is generally regarded as arid; but it is claimed that the total flow of streams in Sinkiang is no less than 10.7×10^{10} m³ per annum.[137] On the other hand, the atmosphere is so dry and the evaporation so great that a depth of 1.6 m is necessary for grain growing. If only one-third of the total flow were utilised, and allowing for the greater depth of water required, this would still give a cultivated area of 2.2 million hectares—not far short of Egypt's. In the Middle East on the other hand, it has been claimed by some (though the claim is disputed) that the particularly favourable circumstances of Iraq will permit 50% of the stream flow to be used. Interesting estimates of cultivated, cultivable, irrigated and irrigable areas in the Middle East, as they were in the 1940s, have been made by Bonnê[138] (Table 32). In an earlier study[139] he estimated the total population which could be supported per hectare of cultivated land, under Middle Eastern conditions, ranging from 2 on the best irrigation lands to 0.5 on the poorest natural rainfall lands. The former figure, however, is obviously too low, as Egypt supports 27 million population on $2\frac{1}{2}$ million hectares and still has cotton to export.

CHAPTER 6

CHARGES FOR WATER

CHARGES made for irrigation water are often well below cost.

The charges[114] made for water from the Bhakra Dam in India have been purely nominal ($0 \cdot 01$–$0 \cdot 03$ c/m³, in comparison with the higher but still low charge of $0 \cdot 06$ on old canals). Although the canal system of the dam was extended to grossly uneconomic lengths for political reasons, the attempt to collect a betterment levy "after one year of collection of instalments had to be held in abeyance on account of widespread political agitation against it. . . . The village of Rattan Heri, where most of the irrigated area was canal-irrigated, had masonry wells and one tube well hardly in use."

In the land benefited by the Hirakud Dam it is proposed to collect, by instalments, a betterment of 185–370 R/hectare—only a small part of the capital cost. In Mysore (where irrigation costs are high) it was at one time customary not to begin an irrigation project unless the owners of two-thirds of the land benefited would agree to pay a betterment charge of over 370 R/hectare. In modern India, however, it is considered that such methods are "incompatible with democracy". For sugarcane growing[15] in Maharashtra a charge is made of $0 \cdot 31$ c/m³; it seems clear that the marginal productivity of water is much higher than this, and that the water could have been better used on other crops. Very low charges, between $0 \cdot 03$–$0 \cdot 06$ c/m³, are also found in Pakistan. Ghulam Mohammad[34] records for the areas which he studies in the Punjab, higher charges averaging $0 \cdot 1$ c/m³, slanted in favour of rice ($0 \cdot 05$) and against the successful cash crop of oil seeds ($0 \cdot 27$).

In Australia[140] charges are more than nominal, though still below cost, averaging $0 \cdot 20$ c/m³ (20 shillings/acre-foot) in New South Wales and $0 \cdot 15$ in most of Victoria (though rising to $0 \cdot 48$ in Nyah and $0 \cdot 58$ in Tresco, where pumping costs were high).

In Southern Italy[56] subsidies meet 1·32 out of a total cost of 2·15 c/m³.

In Lebanon[61] on the other hand (assuming average depth of watering of 0·75 m) farmers have been paying the full cost of 5·93 c/m³ for water pumped from the Litani River. New schemes are proposed which will supply them, at a loss, at 2·1 c/m³ for pumped water and 1·3 c/m³ for gravity-supplied.

In Iran,[53] as already stated, water can be obtained from adits to aquiferous rock, and is usually supplied in return for a share of the crop worth about 0·16 c/m³, which gives the owner a 10% net return on his investment. In vegetable gardens in Tehran however, where the seller of water enjoys an economic rent, the price (calculated on the assumption of a water use of 6 mm/day, or 2·2 m/year) rises to 1·9 c/m³.

Charges made for irrigation water in U.S.A. in 1950 (converted to present-day dollars) showed a range of variations (Table 33).[74]

The authors report large industrial users as paying an average of 3–3·5 c/m³ (minimum 1·5 in Arkansas, maximum 7·4 in Texas). Such users making provision from their own wells incur costs between 1·3 and 2·8 c/m³.

TABLE 33

Charges for Irrigation Water in U.S.A.

	c/m³
Great Basin	0·067
North West	0·074
Upper Missouri	0·087
Upper Arkansas	0·094
Upper Rio Grande	0·134
Colorado River	0·175
Central Pacific	0·201
Western Gulf	0·51
Southern Pacific	0·75
Upper Quartile in Southern Pacific	1·42

Other estimates[72] of average and maximum charges for various users of water are given in Table 34.

TABLE 34

Range of Charges for Water according to use

	Charges in c/m³	
	Average	Maximum
Domestic	9·0	21·2
Industrial	3·6	14·8
Irrigation	0·15	2·43
Power[a]	0·06	0·53
Waste disposal	0·06	0·23

[a] For additional water at a height of 2500 m, however, a power company with a dam already built might find it worth while to pay as much as 6 c/m³ for its power value alone (Strong, *Africa and Irrigation*, 1961, Wright Rain Ltd.)

Most city charges, taking domestic and industrial together, are below 9, and 13·5 c/m³ can be estimated as the upper limit.[141]*

In the Ruhr Valley[71] where a very limited water supply has to be most skilfully managed, to serve the domestic, industrial, navigational and recreational needs of a very large population, the average charge is 8 c/m³.

* However, in the smaller towns water distribution seems to be more costly. Schechter (*Land Economics*, February 1961) found for Tennessee in 1955 charges (in cents of 1964 purchasing power/m³):

Population of town	Under 1000	1–3000	3–5000	5– 10,000	10– 35,000	Over 35,000
Charges	26·0	26·7	24·6	23·0	17·8	10·8

For the United States as a whole, 42% of all cities of size 10–50,000 had charges over 12·5 (in the same units) and 29% of the cities of size 50–100,000. Above that size the proportion remained about 15% irrespective of the size of city. A population of 100,000 appears to be a critical minimum for economic water distribution.

However, McClellan[127] states that the city of Colorado Springs—perhaps an exceptional case—recently offered over 36 c/m³ for water at present being used for agricultural purposes. Koenig, in the same volume (p. 321), quotes a case of a Texas town, in an emergency, paying over 70 c/m³.

> Industry does not have a fixed requirement for water but rather a variable demand which depends importantly on the price of water. Thus, depending on price, steel mills may demand from 6 m³ to 290 m³ water to produce a ton of finished steel; and power plants may use 0·006 to 0·77 m³ to produce a kilowatt-hour of electricity.
>
> In arid regions, irrigation agriculture pays typically very low prices for water and uses huge quantities. In California as a whole, 90 per cent of the water is used for irrigation. The Imperial Valley irrigator, for example, pays 0·16 c/m³ for water while Los Angeles and other cities in a nearby region are paying 2 c/m³ wholesale to the Metropolitan Water District. As for the urban user, distribution costs raise the price to about 6·5 c/m³, and these cities face very much higher costs for future increments of supply.
>
> Inefficiency and waste are strongly indicated when a wide divergence of prices for the same product exist; a difference much greater than the cost of transfer.[142]

An original and valuable new approach to the problem of charging has been made by Wynn[143] working in Sudan. After pointing out that marginal costs of water nearly always differ from average and quoting another American study[144] which indicates that at least half of the present 1 billion m³/year used in irrigating the South Coastal area of California would be uneconomic if users had to pay the marginal cost of incremental supplies now being drawn from the Colorado River, he proposes that the fixed costs of the dam and canal system should be isolated and recouped in the form of a levy on all land *capable* of receiving water from it (at the time when the land becomes capable of irrigation; not during construction; interest during construction is another element in fixed costs). Potential users at the far end of a long and costly canal would have a higher levy to pay—if the original designers of the system knew that such a rule would be put into operation, and that there were limits to what farmers could pay, we might be saved from some uneconomically long canals, as in India. Other costs should then be recouped as a charge per unit of water used. Where a simple barrage is capable of yielding a substantial

water supply (as in Sudan), Wynn suggests that only the estimated cost of such a barrage be included in the fixed costs to
be recovered by the levy on land, and that the more costly
water from the top of the dam should be charged at marginal
cost. The marginal charges also would take account of the
additional seepages and evaporation in long canals. The
tendencies of governments to use water charges for purposes
either of subsidisation or taxation are economically undesirable,
as in the case of Sudan, which taxes cotton, by making it bear
the whole cost of irrigation, and subsidises other crops, by
allowing them water free.

Simpson, in a subsequent issue of the same Journal, tries
unsuccessfully to overthrow Wynn's conclusions. He does,
however, make the interesting point that high marginal costs
for maintenance are more likely to arise in the minor canals
than in the major; the latter run at "non-silting velocities".

De Haven goes on to suggest that the most economical
method of obtaining more water now is the protection of
reservoirs against evaporation by the use of monomolecular
surface films. The use of cetyl alcohol for this purpose in
Australia, where the technique was developed, costs $4 \cdot 9$ c/m^3
(£A25/acre-foot), fully comparable with the cost of new water
in dry areas.

CHAPTER 7

DESALINATION

IT IS against this background of costs and returns that we consider the possibility of obtaining fresh water by distillation from the sea (or other saline water). Complete desalination may not be necessary. Water obtained from tube wells in Pakistan containing $0 \cdot 1\%$ of salt can still be used for irrigation, and $0 \cdot 1$–$0 \cdot 2\%$ if mixed with other water, but it is not practicable to use water containing over $0 \cdot 2\%$.[30] Brackish water containing $0 \cdot 25\%$ salt might be treated[145] with solvents such as pyridine at a cost of $22 \cdot 5$ c/m³; for sea water the cost of such treatment would be 40 c/m³. It was estimated that electrolytic membrane separation,[108] which is not practicable for ocean water, could be carried out at costs as follows:

Salt content %	Costs c/m³
1	$3 \cdot 9$
$0 \cdot 5$	$1 \cdot 9$
$0 \cdot 09$	$0 \cdot 4$

The latter percentage represents the estimated limit for urban water supplies (though such water can still be used for irrigation).* Regarding the content of 1%, such salt concentrations[146] are occasionally found in some areas of the sea (e.g. $0 \cdot 7\%$ in the Baltic, $1 \cdot 5\%$ in Chesapeake Bay). In the lands adjacent to such waters, however, the demand for irrigation water is not generally very high, though the demand for urban water supplies may be. (The average salt content for the oceans is $3 \cdot 5\%$ and for the Persian Gulf $4 \cdot 0\%$.)

However, electrodialysis of brackish mine water in South Africa[147] from $0 \cdot 4\%$ down to $0 \cdot 05\%$ salt content cost 8 c/m³. Treatment of brackish water in South Dakota[148] cost 24–26

---

* Some authorities put the limits for consumption by livestock at $0 \cdot 05$ to $0 \cdot 1\%$, and for human consumption at $0 \cdot 03$ to $0 \cdot 05\%$.

c/m³ however; it was estimated that the process became uneconomic when salt content was higher than 0·3%. The main
difficulties arose, not from the sodium chloride, but from
calcium and magnesium salts.

For distillation the size of plant is important, because
economies of scale are considerable (Table 35).

TABLE 35

Capital Costs of Distillation Plants

	m³/day	Capital cost $/m³/day
Aden	1815	450
Guernsey[a]	2275	375
Bahamas	4550	360
Kuwait	9100	215

Sources: Science News and Bryan, quoted above.

[a] Reduced pressure plant: Bryan estimates that it will deliver water at
one-third the cost of storage.

Costs of fuel alone, Bryan estimated, may be 13–26 c/m³.
With steam from a nuclear reactor, he estimated that total
costs could be brought down to 20 c/m³. Alternatively, waste
heat from generators could be used; the well-known engineering
firm of G. & J. Weir estimated[149] that costs in this way might
ultimately be brought down to 8 c. Richardsons Westgarth,
designing a plant for the Middle East, paying $20/ton for oil,
and generating no power, estimated[149] their costs at 28 c/m³;
selling power at 2·9 c/kWh (quite a high price), they could
reduce the water cost to 3 c/m³.

Koenig points out that to transport such water for a distance
of only 80 km by pumping will lead to additional costs (measured in the same units) of 13–33 c/m³. Transport of the water
for the same distance downhill, by aqueduct, would cost only
0·13–0·2 c/m³. In Israel[73]* it is hoped to bring the cost of

* Israel pound converted at $2/3.

desalinated water down to 11 c/m³ (14 c/m³ delivered) and to produce 2 × 10⁸ m³ annually by 1973.

An interesting and authoritative review[150] of the situation as it was in 1953, with estimates of future possibilities is given in Table 36.

In a paper presented by United Nations Department of Economic and Social Affairs at a conference on desalination in Milan in April 1964, it was stated that costs now were of the order of 25 c/m³, but that the higher engineering costs in developing countries would make the minimum cost there 39 c/m³. The already existing plants reviewed had outputs ranging from 6000 to 20,000 m³/day with costs more or less linearly declining (on a double log scale) from $4/m³ for the smallest to $0·45/m³ for the largest (see Fig. 4). The paper pointed out that although occasionally much higher prices were paid for water (the record being $3·3/m³ paid by a hotel in the Caribbean for water brought by ship) present distillation costs were certainly beyond the reach of agriculture, except in very special cases. On the arid Caribbean island of Aruba distilled water represented 20% of the gross cost of the hydroponic gardens.

A recent proposal[153] for a 50% enlargement to the Kuwait distillation plant (giving another 23,000 m³/day) still showed a marginal cost of 21 c/m³, in spite of the cheapness of fuel.

Meiggs[154] quotes the costs of the Guernsey plant as high as 70 c/m³ (used on the tomato crop only under conditions of unusual emergency) and at Kuwait at 35 c/m³, in spite of having natural gas as free fuel. American municipalities are quoted as paying now for marginal supplies at the rate of 6–10 c/m³, occasionally up to 25.

However, General Dynamics Corporation[155] claim that a large plant to yield 440,000 kW power and 189,000 m³/day fresh water (i.e. power and water for a community of 400,000) could gain greatly in efficiency by using steam at 500 °C. A still larger plant of 2,400,000 kW, paying 10½% for interest plus depreciation, could deliver power at 0·4 c/kWh, and fresh water at 7·1 c/m³.

These claims were substantiated by a report,[156] published in March 1964, of a U.S. Inter-Agency group appointed by President Kennedy, which envisaged a plant using nuclear

TABLE 36

Current and Prospective Costs of Desalination (c/m³)

	Ion Exchange	Multiple effect evapora-tion	Vapour compres-sion	Electrolytic separation	Tempera-ture differ-ence (Claude's method)	Solar evapora-tion	Freezing	Freeport-type plant
Costs in 1953	Over 850	139	75	53	16	38	—	
Estimates made in 1953 of ultimate cost		96	21 (b)	14	11	11	43	
Subsequent costs		Aruba 50 (147) (a)					Israel 14 (151) (c) Tampa 17 (148) (d)	Actual 29 (152) (e) Estimate for future 10 (141) (f)

(a) Output of 10,000 m³/day:
(b) Hickman, quoted in *The Future of Arid Lands*, estimated that this cost could fall to 11.
(c) Fairbanks Whitney plant.
(d) Blaw Knox plant.
(e) Output 4550 m³/day.
(f) For 37,500 m³/day.

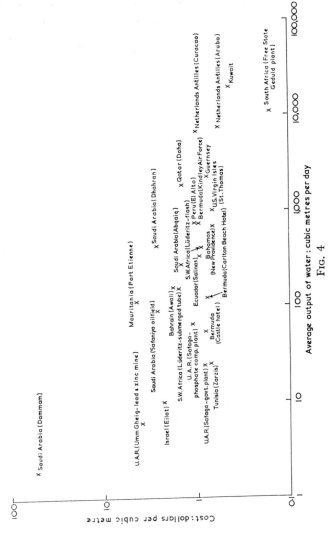

COSTS OF DESALINISATION IN DEVELOPING COUNTRIES

FIG. 4

energy to deliver 1,000,000–1,500,000 kW at $0\cdot23$–$0\cdot25$ c/kWh, and 2–3 million m³/day fresh water at $5\cdot3$–$6\cdot6$ c/m³ (at site). With sufficient expenditure on research and development, such a plant, they estimated, could be in operation by 1975.

While solving the more serious problems of urban water supply, such water, however, would still be beyond the reach of agriculturalists, except for a few specialised crops.

APPENDIX

I AM much indebted to Mr. S. S. Wilson of the Engineering Laboratory, Oxford, for the following information.

The proposition that costs are proportional to depth is generally true provided the proper pump is used; there will, however, be a decrease in costs as size increases, due both to the increase in efficiency and to the probable decrease in capital cost per unit of power. For a pump of given size there is only one depth for efficient operation, depending on the speed of rotation. It is clear that the pump design must be selected according to the depth at which it is to work, but there are virtually no limitations of size or depth.

The table quoted in Chapter 4 refers to the performance of two particular pumps over a range of heads; as expected, the efficiency falls appreciably at high or low heads, and is in fact a maximum for both pumps at about 12 m. However, for other designs of pumps the same best efficiency can be obtained at almost any head from about 2 m upwards; even for a given size and type of pump the point of best efficiency can be moved up or down to different heads by altering the speed, as follows:

$$Q \text{ (flow)} \quad \propto \quad N \text{ (speed)}$$
$$H \text{ (head)} \quad \propto \quad N^2$$
$$P \text{ (power)} \quad \propto \quad N^3$$

For a given design or shape of pump, the performance against a constant head, in terms of a typical dimension, D, the impeller diameter, is:

$$Q \quad \propto \quad D^2$$
$$P \quad \propto \quad D^2$$
$$N \quad \propto \quad \frac{1}{D}$$

A convenient method of estimating the performance of a given design of pump over a range of possible sizes, heads, speeds and flows is the concept of specific speed, defined as the speed at which a model pump would rotate when delivering one unit of flow against one unit head; it can be found from the performance figures of any size of pump, for the point of best efficiency.

$$N_s \text{ (specific speed)} = N\sqrt{Q}/H^{\frac{3}{4}}$$

A disadvantage is that the value of N_s varies according to the units of flow and head used, though there is always a simple multiplication factor to convert from one system of units to another. A better system is Addison's shape number, which is non-dimensional and can be converted easily into any N_s. The name also emphasises that the number is essentially a property of the design or shape of the impeller, and the various types of "rotodynamic" (or distinct from positive-displacement piston pumps). Each have a definite range of shape numbers:

Centrifugal pumps	100–250
Semi-axial or mixed flow	250–500
Propellor or axial pumps	400–800

Within each type different values of N_s imply considerable differences in shape, e.g. 100 would imply a pump for high head and a small flow while higher numbers are associated with lower heads and larger flows. For the very lowest heads, 2–10 m, axial pumps are most suitable, giving smaller pumps, higher speeds and hence smaller and cheaper motors. Semi-axial pumps are suitable for up to 20 m, beyond this centrifugal pumps are suitable; if the head is too great for a single pump, multi-stage types are necessary, and will give good efficiency up to any head required.

Other relevant considerations are that centrifugal pumps may be controlled by throttling and may be safely shut off completely, taking least power under these conditions, though the power may be 50% or more of full power, so the method is wasteful. A recent development is the Dowty vapour-core principle, which effects a great economy in shut-off or low-flow power.

An axial or semi-axial pump should not be controlled by throttling, since the power required rises to a maximum at shut-off, so overloading the motor; they may be controlled by a by-pass circuit allowing re-circulation through the pump.

Axial and semi-axial pumps are much less common than centrifugals; in consequence centrifugal pumps are often cheaper than the other types even if a larger and slow pump is needed. Centrifugals are probably less liable to damage from dirt and silt-laden water.

Although the specific speed concept implies an equal efficiency at the design point condition whatever the size, there will in fact be a variation in efficiency with size. Typical curves showing variation in efficiency both with size and specific speed are shown in, for example, Shepherd, *Principles of Turbomachinery*, Macmillan, N.Y., 1956, Fig. 2–7.

Pump manufacturers publish charts which show quickly and easily the type and size of pump most suitable for any given head and flow, though they do not usually give efficiency—however, this is easily calculated.

It would be technically feasible to supply a range of small pumps which are driven preferably by an 8-pole 400 c/s induction motor from the vapour-cycle power unit.

An indication of the number of permutations possible is given below:

Type	Size B.H.P.	Head	Flow
Centrifugal pump			
Small flow	$\frac{1}{2}$	$6\frac{1}{4}$—$12\frac{1}{2}$ m	3—$1\frac{1}{2}$ l/sec
	to $2\frac{1}{2}$	50	1·86 l/sec
Larger flow	$1\frac{1}{4}$	10—12	5·6—2·8 l/sec
	to $3\frac{3}{4}$	60	5·6—2·8 l/sec
Greatest flow	3	15—30	10—5 l/sec
	to 10	25—50	21—10·5 l/sec
Axial flow pump			
Larger flows,			
lower heads	$\frac{1}{2}$	4	4·7 l/sec
	to 10	10—15	52·5—35 l/sec

Semi-axial pumps could be used for intermediate heads.

Problems of efficiency arise with the smallest pumps.

SUMMARY OF THE ECONOMICS
OF IRRIGATION

IN METRIC units, the supply of a metre depth of water on a hectare of land represents 10,000 m³. British units are not so conveniently inter-related. All measures in this book are made in metric units. Costs are measured in American cents of 1964 purchasing power per cubic metre.* All costs for other countries, or other periods, are converted into cents of 1964 purchasing power by coefficients of the purchasing power of money (which are not the same as the official exchange rates) (Chapter 1).

Rather arbitrary judgements have hitherto been made about the supposed water requirements of different crops. If some crops are grown on unusually porous soils, important differences may arise in water loss by seepage. But otherwise there should be no differences between water requirements of different crops *per day of growing season*, apart from those arising from certain minor factors, such as the crop not completely covering the soil at certain stages of its growth, and the glossiness or roughness of the leaves. For the amount of water which a crop transpires is that required to remove enough heat to keep its temperature down to a bearable level, which in turn depends on the external physical factors of solar radiation, wind, heat storage in the soil, etc. A heavy crop also requires no more water than a light one (pot experiments on this point can be misleading, because they do not reproduce the thermal conditions of the field, where evaporation from one plant helps to cool its neighbours). Also contrary to what is widely believed, crops heavily fertilised with nitrogen require no more water than light crops, and indeed are better able to withstand temporary water shortages.

From the above follows the important economic conclusion that it is always worth while to concentrate irrigation water on the highest-valued and heaviest-growing crops.

* Cited as c/m³.

It is unfortunately not yet possible to construct a production function showing the yield from water supplies at various levels below the optimum. Over-watering not only fails to give any additional yield, but also may, if persisted in, have very serious consequences in raising the water table to plant root level and thus making the land uncultivable, as in large areas of West Pakistan. This can, however, be cured, at considerable expense, by adequate pumping or drainage (Chapter 2).

In commercial agriculture, economic returns to irrigation can be measured in c/m^3, for comparison with costs. In some countries, however, agricultural production is primarily for subsistence rather than for sale; or the prices of crops may be quite out of line with those prevailing in world markets. In these cases, therefore, it is often better to measure the returns per cubic metre of irrigation water supplied in terms of kilograms of wheat equivalent, other agricultural products being expressed in terms of wheat on the ratios prevailing in the world markets.

For the highly sophisticated irrigation agriculture of California, it is possible to prepare linear programmes showing the precise amount of water which it is economical to apply, at various prices of water. These show that at current U.S. farm prices (the results would be different at world prices) a sudden reduction in the utilisation of water occurs when the price of water has risen above $1 \cdot 3$ c/m^3 for small farms, or $1 \cdot 6$ for large farms. Below these prices, it is worth applying water (averaged over the whole farm) at the rate of $1 \cdot 3$ m/year or more; above that, up to a price as high as $2 \cdot 6$ c/m^3, to apply about $0 \cdot 6$ m. Production functions for the factors of production in an Indian village indicated the marginal product of a cubic metre of water at $0 \cdot 25$ kg wheat or $0 \cdot 36$ kg barley (about $1 \cdot 9$ cents at world prices, considerably higher at Indian prices). It is necessary to convert gross crop increments into net marginal returns, which may be very much less, after debiting additional factors of production used for the irrigated crops. Differences between gross and net marginal product are particularly marked in India. The highest returns to irrigation are for potatoes, followed by fruit and vegetables, tobacco, cotton and flax. Returns to irrigation of maize, which is particularly sensitive to water shortages at certain stages of the growing season, can also be high. Generally speaking, however, it is the farmer who already grows high-yielding crops who has most to gain from irrigation (Chapter 3).

Costs of water for irrigation vary very greatly according to whether it is drawn from the flow of streams, pumped from wells of varying depth, or obtained by constructing dams and distribution channels. Spray irrigation, whose technique has recently improved, may be no more costly than furrow irrigation.

The supply of irrigation water both in the United States and in India and Pakistan is seen clearly to be a genuinely "diminishing returns" activity, as the most valuable flowing streams and dam sites will clearly be used first, and sources at increasing costs have to be used as time goes on (though this cost trend may be counteracted by improving techniques of dam construction).

Primitive methods of raising water from wells by man and ox power prove to be barely remunerative even at high Indian prices for grain, at low Indian wages, and with the water table near the surface. However, simple mechanical pumps prove highly remunerative under these circumstances. Pumping costs are lowest if electric power is available—diesel pumps have higher costs both for fuel and for maintenance.

The costs of constructing dams range from 6 to 9 c/m³ of water stored for the smallest dams, to 0·7 for the largest, where a great deal more water is stored per unit volume of dam wall. Unless, however, the water can be distributed down a river system, the per unit cost savings of a large dam are mostly offset by the additional costs incurred for the distribution network and for land levelling. Where a large dam is used both for irrigation and for hydro-electric generation, as is often the case, the best method of analysing the cost is to credit it first with the full capital saving of the alternative thermal generating capacity which would have had to have been constructed if the hydro-electric capacity from the dam had not been available to meet peak loads; together with a more speculative estimate of the capitalised value of the fuel saved by the existence of the hydro-electric power, which of course depends on the estimated number of hours/year for which it operates. The application of this method to large dams and barrages in India, Pakistan and

Ceylon indicates net annual cost of water (taken at 10% of capital cost) varying from $0 \cdot 13$ to $1 \cdot 35$ c/m³. Total costs of irrigation water may range from $0 \cdot 1$ c/m³ for water drawn from the flow of streams in United States and $0 \cdot 16$ in Iran to 11 c/m³ in Britain, where small and very costly schemes prevail (Chapter 4).

The available flow of water in rivers depends, of course, on the rainfall, of which however a considerable amount may evaporate before it reaches the rivers; and unfortunately it is in the areas where water is needed most that the greatest proportion is thus lost. Run-off (river flow) appears to be related to rainfall by a cubic function, proportionate run-off being much higher where rainfall is highest, with different coefficients to the function for different types of topography.

For measuring national water resources, a convenient unit is that which would serve to irrigate a million hectares to 1 m depth annually (10^{10} m³/year). In the United States in 1954, for example, demand for domestic uses was only $2 \cdot 3$ units, of which $2 \cdot 0$ (albeit somewhat contaminated) were returned to the river flows. Industrial demand (principally from steel, oil and paper industries) was twice the domestic, of which, however, all but $0 \cdot 4$ unit were returned to the stream flow. Demand by power stations for cooling water was $10 \cdot 2$ units, of which only $0 \cdot 1$ was evaporated and the rest returned to stream. Agriculture, however, consumed $24 \cdot 2$ units gross and $14 \cdot 3$ units net. Total net use was thus $15 \cdot 1$ units, although power stations and others with a high gross demand needed the flow of rivers to be maintained. It was also estimated that in order to keep the rivers even at a barely tolerable level of cleanliness, as much as another $70 \cdot 7$ units was required for the dilution of industrial and domestic effluents, making a total requirement of $85 \cdot 8$ units. Total stream flow is 187 units, which should on the face of it leave an ample margin. It is, however, least available in the times and places where it is most required. In some of the drier western states water systems are having to be constructed at rapidly mounting costs; and it appears that some irrigation agriculture will have to be abandoned.

India has a stream flow of 167 units, of which only $9 \cdot 3$ were used for irrigation in 1949. It was hoped eventually to raise this to $34 \cdot 7$, about the maximum proportion of stream flow whose use could ever be practicable, in view of the great irregularity of the flow of the rivers. In the cases of the Nile and the Indus, however, in spite of the irregularity of flow, it is hoped eventually to use three-quarters of the flow after the construction of some costly works (Chapter 5).

Charges made for irrigation water by public authorities, being settled by political pressures rather than by market principles, are nearly always well below costs, and often impose considerable indirect economic burdens on the taxpayer, and also on domestic and industrial users, who have to pay cost price for their water, after the irrigators have taken the lion's share of the supplies. Where a dense population has to live on a limited water supply, as in the Ruhr Valley, where an average charge of 8 c/m³ is made, remarkable economies in water use can be made by careful treatment of effluents, and re-use of water. It is found also that the water requirements of industries and power plants are by no means fixed, and can be reduced by factors of fifty or a hundred if water is high-priced. In hot arid areas, the best prospect now for improving water supply may be the checking of evaporation from reservoirs by the use of mono-molecular films, a technique developed in Australia (Chapter 6).

For the brackish water found in certain parts of the world, with a salt content up to 1%, various techniques are available for desalination at a moderate cost. Sea water, however (average salt content $3 \cdot 5\%$), has to be distilled, and costs hitherto have been extremely high, far out of reach of any agriculturalist, except possibly a grower of very high priced fruits and vegetables in a completely arid country. Recent work has suggested, however, that the combination of a nuclear generator and a distillation plant, in an area where there was a good market for both power and water, might reduce the cost of distilled water to 6 c/m³. To this figure, however, would have to be added distribution cost, which would make it still much too costly for agricultural use, though well below the price which municipal authorities are now willing to pay for additional supplies in some arid areas (Chapter 7).

REFERENCES

1. J. C. De Haven, *Journal of American Waterworks Association*, May 1963.
2. *Geographical Review*, Jan. 1948.
3. Penman, private communication.
4. Hunting Technical Services, private communication.
5. Association Internationale d'Hydrologie, Publication 38.
6. Queensland Irrigation and Water Supply Commission, Report on Mareeba-Dimbulah Irrigation Project, 1952.
7. Binnie, Deacon and Gourley, Report to the Government of Iraq Development Board, *Zad Irrigation Project*, Vol. I.
8. Sir M. Macdonald and Partners, Report No. 2 to the Government of Iraq on the Diyala and Middle Tigris Projects, 1958.
9. Jerusalem Conference, Oct. 1953, Data and Plans.
10. Stedman Davies, Middle East Agricultural Development Conference, 1944.
11. (Emilia-Romagna). Perdisa, quoted Tofani, *Genio Rurale*, Aug. 1955.
12. Report to the President of U.S.A. on Land and Water Development in the Indus Plain.
13. Punjab. Director of Irrigation, private communication, 1952.
14. N.W. Frontier Province. Director of Agriculture, private communication, 1952.
15. Gokhale Institute, Poona, private communication.
16. Wright Rain Ltd., private communication.
17. Dr. Cowan, University of Nottingham, private communication.
18. Mr. P. H. T. Beckett, University of Oxford Soil Science Laboratory, private communication.
19. *Journal of Farm Economics*, Aug. 1962.
20. *American Journal of Agronomy*, Nov. 1961.
21. Molenaar, *Irrigation by Sprinkling*, F.A.O. Development Paper No. 65, 1960.
22. E. W. Russell, *Soil Conditions and Plant Growth*, 8th edition.
23. Low and Armitage, *Journal of Agricultural Science*, 1959.
24. Nix, Cambridge Farm Economics Branch Report No. 55 and *Agriculture*, May 1960.
25. Wickizer and Bennett *The Rice Economy of Monsoon Asia*.
26. International Rice Commission, Newsletter No. 8, Dec. 1953.
27. Californian Dept. of Public Works, *Bulletin* No. 27, 1931.
28. Grüner, *Bewässerungs Anlagen*, Zürich, 1944.
29. Ionides, *The Water Resources of Transjordan*.
30. Naylor, *International Journal of Agrarian Affairs*, Oct. 1963.
31. Narayan Aiyar, *Field Crops of India*, Bangalore, 1944.

32. *U.S.A. Department of Agriculture Year Book*, 1955.
33. Anderson, *Agricultural Economic Research*, April 1961.
34. Ghulam Mohammad, *Pakistan Development Review*, Spring 1965.
35. Moore and Hedges, *Agricultural Economic Research*, Oct. 1963.
36. Dawson, *Journal of Farm Economics*, vol. xxix, No. 5, 1957, Proceedings.
37. Hopper, *Journal of Farm Economics*, Aug. 1965.
38. Naik, *Indian Journal of Agricultural Economics*, July–Sept. 1965.
39. Jewett, for Hunting Technical Services, private communication.
40. Waring, *Review of Marketing and Agricultural Economics*, Sydney, Dec. 1959.
41. Mason, *Review of Marketing and Agricultural Economics*, June 1963.
42. New South Wales, *Milk Board Journal*, Feb. 1959.
43. Bird and Mason, *Review of Marketing and Agricultural Economics*, Dec. 1964.
44. Bank of New South Wales, *Spray Irrigation*, 1956.
45. Murrumbidgee Irrigation Authority Publications.
46. Klatzman, *La Localisation des Cultures en France*, INSEE, 1955.
47. Hallaire and Tabard, Académie d'Agriculture de France, 29 Sept. 1961.
48. Indian Statistical Institute Planning Unit, *Price Policy for Irrigation Undertakings. A Preliminary Study*, Aug. 1961.
49. Gokhale Institute Publication No. 17, *Economic Effects of Irrigation*, 1948.
50. Sovani and Rath, Gokhale Institute Publication, *Economics of a Multiple Purpose River Dam*.
51. Professor Gadgil, *Evaluation of the Benefits of Irrigation Projects*, Planning Commission Research Programmes Committee.
52. Board of Economic Inquiry, Punjab, Publication No. 78.
53. Beckett, *Royal Central Asian Society Proceedings*, 1953.
54. Yudelman, *Journal of Farm Economics*, Feb. 1958.
55. *International Institute of Agriculture Monthly Review*, June 1913.
56. Vincinelli, *International Journal of Agararian Affairs*, Jan. 1963.
57. Tofani, *Genio Rurale*, Aug. 1955.
58. Merendi, *Banco di Roma Review*, Nov. 1957.
59. Antonietti, d'Alarmo and Vanzetti, *Carta delle Irrigazioni d'Italia*.
60. Davies, *Economic Geography*, July 1958.
61. Ward, *International Journal of Agrarian Affairs*, June 1959.
62. U.N. Relief Organisation, Beirut, *Quarterly Bulletin*, March 1958.
63. Woudt, *World Crops*, June 1958.
64. Stuart and Haslam, *Lincoln College Publication*, No. 6.
65. Church, *Geographical Review*, 1951.
66. Cleasby, *Africa and Irrigation*, Wright Rain Ltd., 1961.
67. *Agricultural Engineering*, March 1955.
68. *The Agricultural Situation*, Feb. 1953.
69. Committee on Allocation of Construction Changes, U.S. Bureau of Reclamation and State College of Washington, March 1953 (quoted in Bulletin 597 of State College of Agricultural Experiment Stations).

70. A. B. Ritchie, Penshurst, Victoria, private communication, 1961.
71. *Resources* (Resources for the Future, Washington, 1961).
72. Renshaw, *Journal of American Waterworks Association*, March 1958.
73. Weitz, *Economics of Water Supply in the National Economy*, Rehovoth, 1964.
74. Gertel and Wollman, *Journal of Farm Economics*, Dec. 1960.
75. Fortier, *Use of Water in Irrigation*, 1926.
76. Newell and Murphy, *Principles of Irrigation Engineering*, 1913.
77. Bonnal, *Manual of Collective Sprinkler Irrigation* (OECD).
78. Sir Ronald Prain, Rhodesian Selection Trust, private communication.
79. Economic Commission for Latin America, *Technique of Programming Economic Development*.
80. Houston, *Geographical Journal*, Sept. 1954.
81. *Queensland Newsletter*, 3 Sept. 1964.
82. Eildon, *Australian Newsletter*, 25 Oct. 1956.
83. Tinaroo, *Queensland Year Book* 1963.
84. N. Clark, *Large Earth Dams*, Commonwealth Scientific and Industrial Research Organisation, private communication.
85. *The Economic Development of Ceylon* (International Bank).
86. Husein, World Population Conference, 1954.
87. U.N. Relief and Works Agency, Quarterly Report, April 1956.
88. U.N. Economic Developments in the Middle East, 1945–54.
89. El Tonbary, *International Journal of Agrarian Affairs*, Jan. 1961.
90. Issawi, *Egypt at Mid Century*.
91. Sirry Pasha, *Irrigation in Egypt* (Government Press, Cairo, 1937)
92. *Comercio Exterior*, May 1957.
93. Select Committee of National Water Resources, U.S. Senate, Committee Print No. 32 (1960).
94. Geddes, *Outlook on Agriculture* (U.K.), 1964, No. 4.
95. *Finances and Economics of Irrigation Projects*, Punjab Engineering Congress, Lahore, 1939.
96. *India 1961* (Indian High Commissioner's Office, London).
97. *River Valley Projects in India*, Central Waterpower and Irrigation Commission.
98. Pakistan: Department of Irrigation, private communication.
99. Estacio, *International Journal of Agrarian Affairs*, Oxford, June 1959.
100. Professor Zia ud-Din Ahmad, Professor of Geography, University of Lahore, Pakistan, private communication.
101. A. R. Tainsh, Stockholm, private communication.
102. Dias, *Tropical Agriculturalist*, Ceylon, 1956.
103. S. S. Wilson, Engineering Laboratory, Oxford, private communication.
104. Rowland, *Africa and Irrigation*, 1961, Wright Rain Ltd.
105. Shastri, *Economic Weekly*, 29 Oct. 1960.
106. Ghosh, *International Statistical Institute Proceedings*, 1951.
107. Punjab Board of Economic Inquiry, *Economics of Well Irrigation in the Thal*, 1950.

108. Koenig, *The Future of Arid Lands*, American Association for the Advancement of Science, 1956, p. 321.
109. Ghulam Mohammad, *Pakistan Development Review*, Summer, 1964.
110. Punjab Department of Irrigation, private communication, 1952.
111. Blass, *Water Resources of Israel*.
112. Mississippi Agricultural Experiment Station, Circular 181, 1953.
113. Shafi Niaz, Government of Pakistan.
114. Ansari, *International Journal of Agrarian Affairs*, Oct. 1963.
115. P. C. Bansil, private communication.
116. Kanwar Sain, private communication.
117. *New Scientist*, 1 Oct. 1964.
118. Hickey, *Village in Vietnam*.
119. Etcheverry and Harding, *Irrigation Practice and Engineering*, 1933.
120. Pair, *World Crops*, April 1962.
121. Prof. Isaac, University of Durham, private communication.
122. Ingersent, *Economic Aspects of Farm Irrigation*, University of Nottingham, 1964.
123. *Econometrica*, Oct. 1957.
124. Colas, *Population*, Jan.–March 1964.
125. Pearson and Harper, *The World's Hunger*, 1945.
126. White, *Geographical Review*, Oct. 1957.
127. McClellan, *The Future of Arid Lands*, American Association for the Advancement of Science, 1956.
128. Tixeront, *The Future of Arid Lands*, American Association for the Advancement of Science, 1956.
129. Rural Reconstruction Commission, 1944.
130. Roederer, *Hydrologie du Maroc*, 1952, quoted Houston, *Geographical Journal*, Sept. 1954.
131. *Wald und Wasser*, 1958.
132. Lang, *Journal of Institute of Engineers*, Australia, March 1946.
133. Shen, Agricultural Development in Taiwan.
134. *New Commonwealth*, 19 Aug. 1954.
135. Davies, *Geographical Journal*, Nov. 1958.
136. *The Times*, 9 Nov. 1959.
137. Chang Chih-yi, *Geographical Review*, 1949.
138. Bonné, *Middle East Review*, Winter, 1951.
139. Bonné, in *L'Égypte Contemporaine*, 1942.
140. *Review of Marketing and Agricultural Economics*, Sept. 1959.
141. Ackerman and Löf, *Technology in American Water Development*.
142. James C. de Haven, *Journal American Water Works Association*, 5 May 1963.
143. Wynn, *Sudan Agricultural Journal*, June 1965.
144. Hirschleifer de Haven and Millman, *Water Supply Economics Technology and Policy* (1960).
145. University of Maryland, *Studies in Business and Economics*, Dec. 1958.
146. Jenkins, *Scientific American*, March 1957.
147. Bryan, *New Commonwealth*, Sept. 1959.
148. *New York Times*, 21 Feb. 1963.

149.   *Manchester Guardian*, 27 Feb. 1962.
150.   Rand Corporation Publication, R. 258.
151.   *U.S. News and World Report*, 21 Dec. 1959.
152.   *Science News Letter*, vols. 75, 77.
153.   *International Financial News Survey*, 21 Jan. 1966.
154.   Meiggs, *Geographical Review*, Oct. 1965.
155.   San Diego, California, Press Release, 13 July 1964.
156.   *The Times* (London), 25 June 1964.

INDEX

H